THE COMPLETE GUIDE TO

ELECTRO-EPILATION

ANGELA WHEAT
DRE, MIE, CERT ED.

Hodder & Stoughton

A MEMBER OF THE HODDER HEADLINE GROUP

For the reproduction of copyright material the publishers would like to thank the following:

Ross and Wilson: Anatomy and Physiology in Health and Illness, Waugh and Grant, (Copyright 2002), by permission of the publisher Churchill Livingstone; Nelson Thornes Ltd for the extract from *Principles and Techniques for the Electrologist* by Ann Gallant ISBN 0859504891, first published in 1983; from *Milady's Standard Textbook for Professional Estheticians, 8th edition*, by J. Gerson, copyright 1999. Reprinted with permission of Delmar a division of Thomson Learning. Fax 800 730-2215.

Orders: please contact Bookpoint Ltd, 130 Milton Park, Abingdon, Oxon OX14 4SB. Telephone: (44) 01235 827720, Fax: (44) 01235 400454. Lines are open from 9.00–6.00, Monday to Saturday, with a 24 hour message answering service. Email address: orders@bookpoint.co.uk

British Library Cataloguing in Publication Data
A catalogue record for this title is available from The British Library

ISBN 0 340 803 622

First published 2002

Artworks by David Hancock

Photographs appear courtesy of: Wellcome Trust Medical Photographic Library; National Medical Library and the Science Photo Library.

Images of specialist equipment supplied courtesy of Ellison's.

Cover photo: copyright Douglas Kirkland/ Corbis

Typeset by Servis Filmsetting Ltd, Manchester.

Printed in Great Britain for Hodder & Stoughton Educational, a division of Hodder Headline Plc, 338 Euston Road, London NW1 3BH by Martins The Printers Ltd, Berwick upon Tweed.

Contents

Chapter Three

A study of the structure of the skin and hair   33

Chapter Four

Dermatology   53

Chapter Five

Equipment 67

Chapter Six

Hygiene and Legislation 81

Chapter Seven

The consultation 99

Chapter Fifteen

Acknowledgements

I wish to thank the many people who encouraged and supported me whilst writing this book.

Firstly, my husband Brian who has always been a tower of strength to me over the years, and steadfastly supported me throughout my career. My children Sarah-Louise and Adam who have encouraged me, always giving me a constant supply of patience, understanding and love, regardless of the missed weekends etc, just to say I promise to be more attentive from now on and relax and enjoy family life once again.

To my mother Sadie for always being there when we need her and for her continued love and support.

To my colleagues at West Kent College for their support, especially Glynis Turpin DRE who encouraged me and generously contributed her precious time, knowledge and vast experience to chapters 12 and 13 as well as reviewing text for me, my grateful thanks.

Rose Knutton and Hilary Cowley: valued colleagues and good friends who reviewed the text.

Jane Cochran for her advice on chapters 2 and 4.

Joanne England for her ability to interpret my drawings and ideas and produce my teaching aids etc.

My thanks to Jan Jones DRE for so generously offering her precious time to review each chapter and the encouragement she offered me whilst writing this book.

Also to Marianne Kelly DRE who many years ago encouraged me to extend my knowledge by upgrading my electrolysis skills to DRE standard, setting me on the most enjoyable and rewarding career path possible.

Bob Woodhouse for his advice.

Last but not least my best friends Sue Ticknor and Joanne Paice who have always believed in my ability to write this book and encouraged me to complete it.

Ellisons for supplying photographs of equipment.

Preface

This book has been written firstly for the student electrologist or beauty therapist studying electrolysis either at college or within the work place to level 3, its equivalent and above. Secondly, for qualified practitioners and teachers who wish to update or extend their knowledge. It covers all aspects of electro-epilation including a basic knowledge of the latest advances in alternative hair removal treatments, namely laser and intense pulsed light therapy. There are revision questions or tasks at the end of each chapter for students to review their own learning, with model answers for all questions located within chapter 15.

Electrolysis can be described as a specialist field of beauty therapy, which not every student is capable of mastering. Students need a natural aptitude for this type of work, because electrolysis in the wrong hands is a licence to maim. This book has, therefore, been designed to provide comprehensive theoretical and practical underpinning knowledge to equip students with the essentials to work safely, effectively and professionally.

The history of electro-epilation

The origins of electro-epilation were pioneered in 1875 by an ophthalmologist, Dr Charles Michel, in St Louis, Missouri, America. Dr Michel found that by inserting a needle charged with a negative galvanic current into a hair follicle, he was able to remove ingrowing eyelashes permanently. It was initially thought that the hairs had been electrocuted, but it was subsequently established that using a direct electrical current in a solution of saline water caused the water and salt to divide into their chemical elements and then quickly rearrange themselves to form new substances. Namely sodium hydroxide – a strong caustic alkali which chemically decomposed the hairgrowth – and hydrochloric acid. This process was termed 'electrolysis'.

Eleven years later in 1886 Dr George Fox published an article on galvanic epilation 'the use of electricity in the removal of superfluous hair and the treatment of various facial blemishes'.

Then in 1895, the first training course for electrolysis was written by Daniel Mahler of Rhode Island, America.

In 1916 the multiple needle technique was introduced, invented by Professor Paul Kree. This technique allowed as many as 10 needles to be inserted simultaneously into hair follicles, which revolutionised the previously slow process of electrolysis and made it a more practical method of treatment for hair removal.

In 1924, a new method of electrolysis was introduced by Dr Henry Bordier, in Lyons, France. He pioneered the use of shortwave diathermy to remove unwanted hair growth. This proved to be a much quicker method of hair removal even when compared with the Kree multiple needle technique, and soon superseded galvanic.

Over the next 20 years shortwave diathermy technology continued to advance, with the introduction of a new high frequency alternating current during the 1940's. This new type of machine proved to be a more reliable method of hair removal and helped to firmly establish shortwave diathermy as the market leader.

In 1945, Arthur R. Hinkle and Henri E. St Pierre patented the first combination current machine called the blend. This method of electrolysis became firmly established in America, and was not generally introduced to England until the 1980's, although one or two prominent electrologists did undertake its use and begin training programmes. It was only during the mid 1990's that it became more widely used within salons . . .

Causes of hairgrowth | 1

Women all over the world have, for many years, been experiencing some form of hairgrowth problem. This chapter offers an insight into the causes of hairgrowth and the types of unwanted hairgrowth that can be presented to the electrologist.

The Problem

For many centuries, women have removed unwanted hairgrowth. This can be dated as far back as the ancient Greeks, Romans and Eygptians, who removed hair by rubbing a pumice stone over the skin's surface.

Today it is estimated that up to 85 per cent of women worldwide remove unwanted hairgrowth by one method or another. Society shapes the way we feel and see ourselves and excess or superfluous body hairgrowth has a strong association with masculinity. For women with this problem it undermines their own belief in their femininity and can lead to deep psychological problems.

Excess hairgrowth in women can be unacceptable, and is dependant on culture. For example, some Mediterranean and Middle Eastern countries consider facial or body hairgrowth in women natural, sexy or necessary for personal hygiene. Whilst Northern European and American countries generally consider excess hairgrowth in females unacceptable. In fact during the 1990's, it became even less fashionable for men to have body hair and a percentage of men had chest and back hair removed through waxing.

Whilst excess hairgrowth is a problem for both men and women, society generally finds it more acceptable for a man to have excess body hair than a woman. Unfortunately for women changes in their life cycle – such as puberty, pregnancy and menopause – can bring about excess hairgrowth, as well as systemic illness and medications such as the contraceptive pill and fertility treatment.

There is a need for society to be more sympathetic to hairgrowth problems and this includes the medical profession. Many women and men seek medical advice and depending on the GP may receive little help, whilst others with a sympathetic GP may be referred to a competent electrologist who will be able to achieve long-term clearance of the problem.

Normal systemic causes of hairgrowth

These are puberty, pregnancy and the menopause, which bring about various changes, including hairgrowth (which may be stimulated or inhibited depending on hormone sensitivity).

The areas affected during hormonal changes include:
✧ The axilla/underarm
✧ The pubic area
✧ The breasts/chest
✧ The shoulders and back in men
✧ Thighs and lower legs
✧ Facial areas, top lip, chin and neck.

Puberty

This affects the female in many ways. The pituitary gland secretes its gonadotrophic hormones that act on the ovaries to produce the hormones oestrogen and progesterone. This leads to the formation of breasts and the onset of menstruation along with other physical changes. (see chapter 2 for more details).

The adrenal glands also secrete the hormone androgen, which leads to the development of hairgrowth on the body, axillae and pubic regions.

Any hairgrowth occurring during this period, is due to the fine vellus hairgrowth being stimulated to form accelerated vellus or shallow terminal hairs. This is due to either a hormonal imbalance or follicle sensitivity to normal levels of circulating androgens.

Any hormone imbalance is usually only temporary, while the ovaries and adrenal glands learn to co-ordinate together. If the hairgrowth is left alone it may not become a problem. However, if treated with a temporary method of hair removal, it will given time, be stimulated to form a deep terminal hair that will require regular electrolysis treatment.

Pregnancy

Due to the sudden change in the balance of hormones that is brought about during pregnancy by the excessive activity within the endocrine system, there is often an excess of androgen hormones produced. Fine excess hairgrowth may occur at this time on the top lip, chin, sides of the face, breast and abdomen according to individual's sensitivity to circulating androgens. These hairs rarely become terminal and usually disappear after childbirth when the hormonal stimulus ceases.

Some women do in fact produce less body hair whilst pregnant and have a form of mild alopecia.

Menopause

This occurs around the age of 45+, when the ovaries reduce their levels of the hormone oestrogen as their reproductive life is coming to an end. Oestrogens have the effect of reducing the rate of hairgrowth and diameter of hairs, as well as inhibiting androgen secretion. Thus, hairgrowth tends to occur during this period as oestrogen levels decline and Androgen levels become more influential, promoting hairgrowth in the male pattern top lip and chin mainly. Not all women will experience this problem only those more sensitive to circulating Androgens.

Abnormal systemic changes

These are diseases or disorders within the endocrine system, which may arise as a result of internal or external influence, and can bring about an imbalance of hormonal levels leading to various conditions. The diseases and disorders include:

✧ Ovarian cysts or tumours
✧ Adrenal tumour
✧ Anorexia nervosa
✧ Diabetes mellitus
✧ Cushing syndrome
✧ Adrenal genital virilism syndrome
✧ Drugs.

All of these may result in an abnormal level of hairgrowth. We will cover endocrine disorders in chapter 2.

Causes of hairgrowth

There are generally three factors that cause an increase in hairgrowth, they are:

✧ The genetic hormonal make-up we are born with.
✧ Stimulation of hair follicles through an increased blood supply.
✧ Stimulation due to either increased hormonal levels or sensitivity to hormones circulating within the bloodstream.

Hereditary

We are born with a genetic make-up from our parents. This determines if we are to be fair haired with an average percentage of body hair or dark haired with an unusually high percentage of body hair or vice versa. Genetic make-up is also determined by our race. If we are Italian, Indian or Scandinavian, our hairgrowth will be different.

Topical stimulation

This is any form of temporary treatment applied to the skin's surface which stimulates an increase in the local blood supply. Treatments such as plucking, waxing or even a plaster cast on a broken leg, will stimulate vellus hairgrowth to develop into deep terminal hair growth with time. Also, some medicated creams when applied to the skin can stimulate hairgrowth for example, steroid-based creams.

Medication

Some drugs can promote hairgrowth to develop in the male pattern, due to their effect on the internal system, including:

✧ A wide range of steroid medication
✧ Oral contraceptives, artificial hormones
✧ Hormone replacement therapy (HRT) drugs
✧ Some drugs for the treatment of epilepsy
✧ Drugs for treatment of endometriosis
✧ Drugs for the treatment of breast cancer
✧ Some fertility treatment drugs
✧ Generally any drugs that have androgenic properties (androgens will stimulate hair-growth and increase their diameter).

Severe emotional trauma

This occurs when women are put under emotional stress such as divorce, death etc. During periods of prolonged stress women may develop excess hairgrowth due to high levels of adrenalin being produced within the medulla of the adrenal glands. This, in turn, leads to the adrenal cortex producing large quantities of the male hormone group androgens, which in turn leads to hairgrowth in the male pattern if the individual is sensitive to these increased levels of circulating androgens. This hairgrowth may regress when the source of stress ceases, if the hair is not tampered with.

Surgical changes

The removal or reduction of specific endocrine glands. The most common being a hysterectomy where both the ovaries and uterus are removed or the removal of one or both ovaries. This leads to a sudden decline in oestrogen levels and may result in unwanted hairgrowth, due to the hormone androgen no longer being suppressed by the hormone oestrogen. This procedure can bring about a hormonal imbalance that may need medical supervision. Any hormonal imbalance can have an affect on hairgrowth.

Hirsutism

This condition refers to the male pattern of hairgrowth. When this condition occurs in women, it affects hormone-dependant terminal hairs in localised areas. Usually occurring just before or after puberty, it can be caused by an endocrine disorder or increased sensitivity to circulating androgen hormones. Women with this condition may develop coarse thick hair growth in any area of the body associated with the male hair pattern, for example top lip, chin, neck and breast etc.

There are two forms of hirsutism: primary and secondary.

Primary: when there is increased follicle sensitivity to normal levels of circulating androgens in the bloodstream. This occurs around puberty and stabilises around 30 years of age.
Secondary: occurs after puberty and is due to endocrine disorders such as ovarian or adrenal tumours. This may raise levels of the male hormones androgen and testosterone, secreting these high levels directly into the bloodstream causing sudden virilisation.

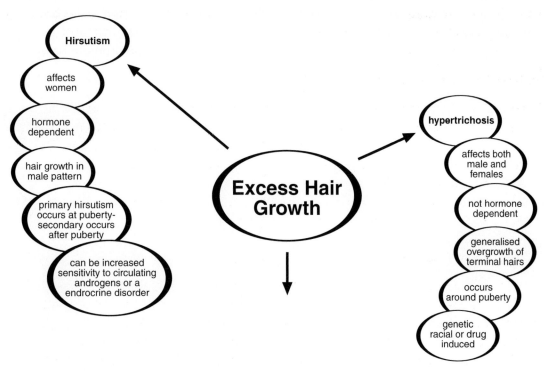

Excess hairgrowth in male/female

Treatment

It requires rapid medical attention, which may be in the form of drugs or surgery. Medical treatment will prevent further vellus hairs being activated into deep terminal hairgrowth, but it cannot reverse hairgrowth already in this stage. This will require the expertise of a competent electrologist under medical supervision.

Hypertrichosis

This is a generalised overgrowth of terminal hairs, which are non-sexual, inappropriate and unacceptable for the individual's age and sex. It is found in both men and women where hormone levels are normal. It begins around puberty and gradually becomes more noticeable with time. Many women, and a percentage of men, will require treatment from an electrologist and medical advice.

Hairs grow longer and faster than normal, but there is no increase in the hair thickness (diameter). This is because this condition is not hormone dependant, but due to genetic, hereditary factors and drugs generally. For example, Mediterraneans and some Scandinavians have a greater number of hair follicles and therefore denser vellus body hair, where as Orientals and Afro-Caribbeans have naturally sparser body hair. Just as Indian people have more body hair than English people. For drugs which can promote hairgrowth review Causes of hairgrowth beginning on page 3.

reviewquestions

Q1 State five causes of hairgrowth.

Q2 What percentage of women on average remove unwanted hairgrowth?

Q3 Name one drug that may induce unwanted hairgrowth.

Q4 A female suffering with hirsuitism is likely to have hairgrowth in which areas?

Q5 Explain the effect of the hormone androgen on the rate and diameter of hairgrowth.

Q6 Hypertrichosis is likely to affect which sex?

Q7 State one possible cause of hypertrichosis.

Q8 In which year was electrolysis first developed?

Q9 Which decade was the blend technique introduced to England?

Q10 State two examples of topical stimulation.

Q11 Briefly explain why medical support is ideally required for some women suffering from excess unwanted hairgrowth.

Q12 Describe the type of hairgrowth present with the condition hypertrichosis.

The endocrine system | 2

This chapter introduces you to the endocrine system. It is essential for the electrologist to have a good understanding of the endocrine system, as we need to be able to recognise the symptoms of endocrine disorders and the effects of stress etc, to determine the most appropriate method of epilation to be used, and if medical referral is required.

Endocrine comes from the Greek word for 'internal secretion' and within the body there are a series of endocrine glands. These glands secrete chemicals that have a wide effect on the body's metabolism. These secretions are known as hormones, which comes from the Greek 'to excite' and they can increase or decrease the metabolism of the body, altering the functioning of the body so that efficient co-ordination is not always possible. These endocrine glands are known as ductless glands, because they secrete their hormones directly into the bloodstream where they become attached to the plasma proteins and are transported around the body to a specific organ, where they stimulate a reaction.

Hormones are chemical messengers and differ from the nervous system in co-ordination, in that their reactions are not always rapid. For example, the growth hormone and thyroxine produce a slow effect over a period of time. Adrenaline has a speedy instantaneous effect, but is influenced by nervous stimuli.

Chemically, hormones also differ from one another, some are derived from amino acids whilst others are from a group of chemicals called steroids. In the most part they function in partnership with one or more hormones, and not independently. For example, several different hormones work together to prepare the breast for breast feeding. The activity of the endocrine system is ultimately controlled by the nervous system. The hypothalamus links the endocrine system with the cerebral cortex.

The main endocrine glands are:
✧ the pituitary gland
✧ the thyroid gland
✧ the parathyroid glands
✧ the adrenal glands
✧ the ovaries
✧ the islets of Langerhans
✧ the testes
✧ the thymus gland
✧ the pineal gland.

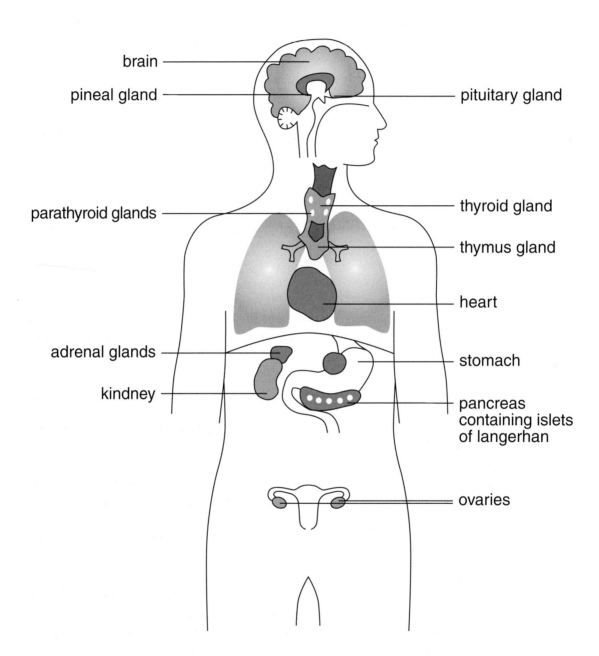

The Endocrine System
female body

brain

pineal gland — pituitary gland

parathyroid glands — thyroid gland

— thymus gland

— heart

adrenal glands — stomach

kindney — pancreas containing islets of langerhan

— ovaries

The endocrine system

The hypothalamus

Location: situated mid brain between the thalamus and pituitary gland, linking the cerebral cortex (in two areas: emotions and motivation), with the pituitary gland and endocrine system, by a stalk richly supplied with blood vessels and nerve fibres.

Structure: composed of a group of nerve cells.

Functions: co-ordinates the autonomic nervous system with the endocrine system and is responsible for the following:

✧ the autonomic nervous system, which regulates our organs' automatic actions, for example: heartbeat, breathing, motor reflexes etc

✧ the normal body temperature, it acts as a thermostat

✧ it is the centre of osmo-regulation, water balance. The body contains a constant volume of water to maintain a fluid balance, therefore water intake and loss must be equal

✧ appetite and thirst, when water in the blood plasma drops we experience the sensation of thirst

✧ metabolic processes

✧ the emotions

✧ the wakefulness and sleep pattern

✧ the regulation of sexual function

✧ the secretion of hormones from the pituitary gland, which exercises control over the endocrine system.

The hypothalamus's influence over the pituitary gland

The hypothalamus produces hormones which have two very different effects on the functioning of the pituitary gland. These hormones regulate and balance the pituitary gland and endocrine system. They are called releasing and inhibiting hormones or factors.

The releasing hormones are triggered when a particular hormone level falls within the bloodstream. It is detected by the hypothalamus which directs the pituitary gland to increase its secretions of a trophic hormone, in order to stimulate hormone production by the target gland, for example low levels of the hormone thyroxine in the blood would trigger the hypothalamus to inform the pituitary gland to increase its secretion of thyroid-stimulating hormone (TSH), which, in turn stimulates the thyroid gland to produce and release the hormone thyroxine. When the correct levels of thyroxine in the blood have been reached, it is detected by the hypothalamus which informs the pituitary gland to inhibit secretions of TSH. This is called negative feedback. Thus, both these releasing and inhibiting hormones help to balance the endocrine system via the pituitary gland. However, external and internal influences can alter the mechanism of the hypothalamus and pituitary gland, such as stress, emotional factors and disease.

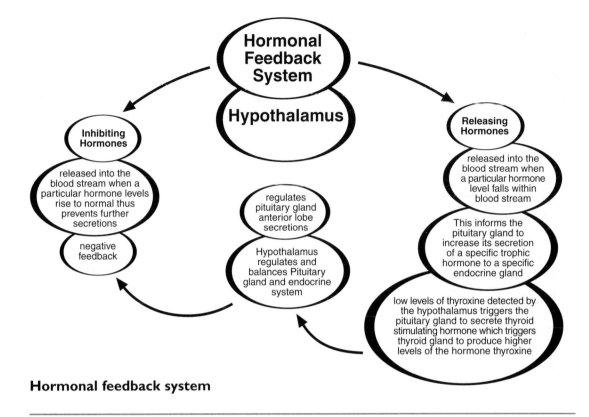

Hormonal feedback system

The pituitary gland

This gland is also known as the master gland as it controls all other endocrine glands and their functions. It has two lobes, the anterior and the posterior.

Structure: the anterior lobe is the larger portion and is composed of vascular and glandular tissue and receives its blood supply from the internal carotid artery via the hypothalamus. Whilst the posterior lobe is composed of nerve-like tissue supplied from the hypothalamus and receives its blood supply also from the internal carotid artery.

Location: at the base of the brain just below the hypothalamus resting in the sphenoid bone and is about 1 cm in diameter. It is attached to the brain by a short stalk.

The posterior lobe/hypophysis: stores two hormones oxytocin and vasopressin.

Oxytocin: produced during childbirth (labour), stimulates muscle contraction of the womb/uterus and also aids the flow of milk after the birth by simulating the cells lining the ducts of the breasts behind the nipples. This hormone works in conjuction with several other hormones to help in the production of milk, including insulin, thyroxine, corticosteriods, oestrogen and progesterone.

Vasopressin/antidiuretic hormone: this hormone is concerned with maintenance of the body's water balance. It increases the permeability of the kidney tubules, so that reabsorption of the water from the glomerus filtrate is increased and no water passes into the blood-stream, thus concentrating urine. It also causes contraction of the involuntary muscles in the bladder and intestines. The amount of vasopressin secreted is influenced by the osmotic pressure of the blood circulating to the osmoreceptors in the hypothalamus. As the osmotic pressure rises the secretions of vasopressin increase and more water is reabsorbed. If osmotic pressure of the blood is low, the secretion of vasopressin is reduced and less water is reabsorbed and more urine is produced. Factors which influence the secretion of this hormone are pain and emotional stress.

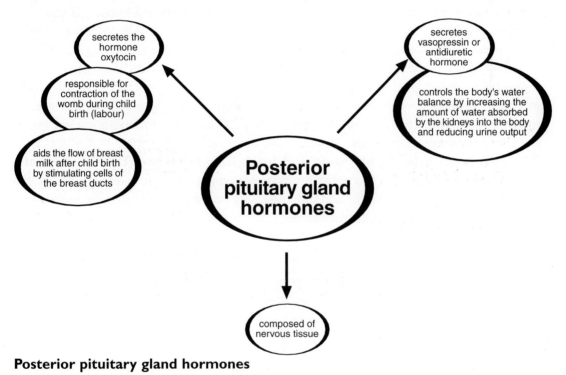

Posterior pituitary gland hormones

The anterior lobe/adenohypophysis: of the pituitary gland secretes six groups of hormones that control and co-ordinate the functions of the endocrine system as follows:

✧ **The growth hormone (GH)** is released by the pituitary gland (after stimulation from the hypothalamus growth hormone releasing factor). It directly affects tissue by stimulating the growth of skeletal bones, the formation of muscles, tissues and organs etc.

✧ **The thyroid-stimulating hormone (TSH)** targets the thyroid gland to produce thyroxine and regulates the activities of the thyroid gland. Again this hormone is only released by the pituitary gland after simulation by the hypothalamus thyroid releasing factor.

✧ **The adrenocorticotrophic hormone (ACTH)** stimulates the blood supply to the adrenal cortex and controls the activities of this gland's cortex and its production of a large number of steroids, especially cortisol.

✧ **The melanocyte-stimulating hormone (MSH)** is responsible for the depth of colour density within the hair and skin and is stimulated during pregnancy and can be seen as chloasma or the linea nigra.

✧ **The gonadotrophic hormones (sex hormones)** are two sex hormones secreted by the pituitary gland in both males and females, the follicle stimulating hormone and the luteninising hormone.

✧ **The follicle-stimulating hormone (FSH)** in the female: The follicle-stimulating hormone stimulates the growth of the Graafian follicle, which releases its own hormone, oestrogen, into the bloodstream, as it grows during the first half of the menstrual cycle, until high levels of oestrogen are detected in the bloodstream by the hypothalamus. This leads to a reduction in FSH levels by the pituitary gland and the release of the luteinising hormone, which triggers ovulation, the release of the now mature egg (ovum) and the simultaneous formation of the corpus luteum, which in turn secretes the hormone progesterone. High levels of progesterone inhibit the luteinising hormone, which results in a drop in progesterone levels and the breakdown of the corpus luteum, triggering menstruation, when fertilization has not occurred. This is a continuous cycle through out the female reproductive life.

✧ **The follicle-stimulating hormone and luteinising hormone (LH) in the male.** The follicle-stimulating hormone has a similar action in men as it is responsible for the growth of spermatozoa (sperm) and the luteinising hormone stimulates the male testes to secrete the sex hormone, testosterone.

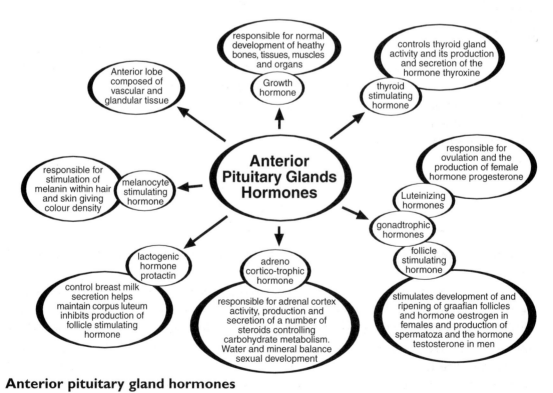

Anterior pituitary gland hormones

✧ **The lactogenic hormone/prolactin.** Prolactin controls the secretion of milk, and maintains the existence of the corpus luteum during pregnancy. It is stimulated by the suckling of the new born baby at the breast and works in conjunction with several hormones to produce breast milk.

Pituitary gland disorders

Pituitary gland disorders usually arise as a result of a tumour causing excess secretions of anterior lobe hormone in particular the growth hormone.

Hypersecretion of growth hormone

If there is an excess of the growth hormone during childhood, when the long bones of the body are still growing it leads to giantism – excessive growth of the long bones. However, if there is an increase in growth hormone levels after our bones have finished growing (gone through ossification) then the condition which results is called acromegaly, which is the abnormal enlargement or thickening of the feet, hands, jaw bone and thickening of soft tissue.

Hyposecretion of growth hormone

If there are insufficient levels of the growth hormone during childhood, growth of the long bones will be stunted and a small person will develop, referred to as a dwarf lorain. However, another condition can arise when there are low levels of the growth hormone thyroxine and the gonadtrophic hormones FSH and LH. This is called a dwarf frôhlich, which is an extremely rare condition with the following symptoms:
✧ retarded mental and sexual development
✧ stunted growth and obesity
✧ knock knees and early senility.

The thyroid gland

Location: Situated either side of the trachea at the lower end of the neck at the front and has two lobes.
Structure: Composed of hollow spherical sacs called follicles, held together by connective tissue containing blood capillaries. The follicle walls are made up of simple cubical epithelial tissue. The epithelial cells secrete the hormone thyroxine into the cavity of the follicle where it is stored in a protein jelly-like substance, and later passed into the bloodstream and transported to the target organs. A fibrous capsule surrounds the gland. There is a good blood supply to the gland from the carotid and subclavian arteries.

Pituitary Gland Abnormalities

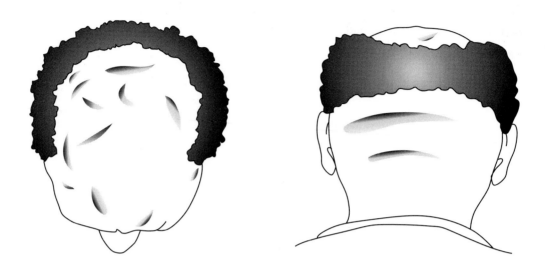

Acromegaly thickening of skin tissues

Enlarged jaw, ears, thickening and coarsening of features and skin tissue.

Pituitary gland abnormalities

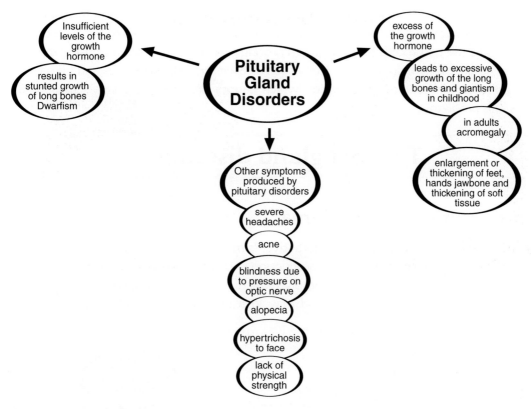

Pituitary gland disorders

The functions of the thyroid gland

✧ to produce and store the hormone thyroxine
✧ stores iodine after removing it from the blood (found in food and water of the diet)
✧ exercises control over the general rate of the metabolism
✧ controls the growth of nervous tissue and mental development during infancy
✧ affects the irritability of the nervous system in adult life, for example calm, highly-strung etc
✧ controls and regulates the growth of the body's bone structure during childhood
✧ works in conjunction with the other endocrine glands to balance the body's systems
✧ maintains the skin and hair's healthy appearance and condition.

The thyroid gland removes iodine from the bloodstream, which receives it from food and water in the diet. The iodine passes into the follicles of the thyroid gland and combines with amino acid – thyrosine – to form the hormone thyroxine. Thyroxine contains a substance, which acts on the basal metabolic rate and the nervous system. Thyroxine's function is to increase the rate at which carbohydrates are oxidised within the tissues to produce energy and stimulates the tissue cells to break down proteins into energy, instead of using them to build new tissue. Some land-locked regions such as Switzerland, the Andes and Himalayas have a deficiency in iodine in the water, which causes an 'endemic goitre'. Iodised salt resolves this problem.

Thyroid gland disorders

Hyposecretion/myxoedema

In this condition the thyroid gland is underactive. It may be due to a deficiency of iodine in the diet. This causes a lack of thyroxine production and secretion, which in turn affects the metabolic rate, slowing it down considerably (which may result in a goitre-swelling in the neck). The individual feels lethargic, and may lose mental agility and become slow to

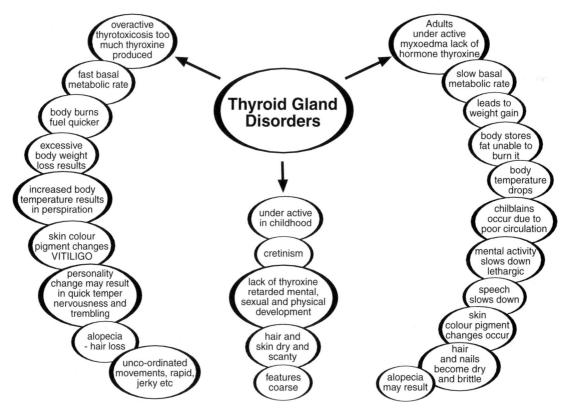

Thyroid gland abnormalities

respond to verbal questions. There is a weight gain as the metabolism is unable to use fat reserves and oxygen, thus the individual becomes obese and oedema may occur. The body temperature is lowered due to the slowing down of metabolic rate, the circulation is poor resulting in individual feeling cold and often displaying chilblains, also blood cholesterol may rise. The skin colour tone may also change becoming yellow (carotineamia). There is often thickening of the skin, which becomes dry and scaly and baldness (alopecia) may develop in some cases. The nails often become dry and brittle.

In childhood lack of thyroxine would result in a condition known as cretinism. In which mental, physical and sexual development are retarded. The tongue may appear protruding and too large, from a sagging mouth. Features are generally coarse with scanty hairgrowth and dry skin.

Thyrotoxicosis/hyper-secretion

This is over activity of the thyroid gland, which may be caused by a tumour in the gland, or it may be due to malfunction of the pituitary gland, which controls the thyroid gland activities. Too much thyroxine is produced and secreted into the bloodstream, which in turn speeds up the metabolic rate, using protein as a source of energy. This leads to excessive weight loss, as the body is in overdrive. The thyroid gland often forms a goitre due to over working. There may be little co-ordination between movements, which are frequently rapid and uncontrolled, also trembling of the hands may be observed. The eyes may also be affected appearing to bulge or protrude from their sockets, due to fluid building up behind the eye balls. Due to an increase in the metabolic rate the body temperature is raised and the skin becomes shiny through excess perspiration. Hair loss may also occur and pigmentation loss of the skin and hair can also result (vitiligo). The individual may also undergo personality changes becoming nervous, edgy and quick tempered, due to the irritability of the nerves being affected. This condition affects other endocrine glands, for example: the ovaries and may cause menstrual disturbances.

Parathyroid glands

Location: Neck region, embedded on the posterior surface of the thyroid gland.
Structure: Composed of four small pea size glands which produce the hormones parathormone and calcitonin.
Function: These two hormones control levels of calcium ions in the blood and other body fluids such as salts and phosphates. They achieve this by releasing calcium ions from bone tissue, increasing calcium reabsorption in the kidney tubules and increasing calcium absorption from food in the intestines. Parathormone (parathyrin) raises the calcium level in the blood. A high level of calcium in the blood suppresses parathormone secretions from the parathyroid glands. Calcitonin is released when calcium levels drop.

Parathyroid abnormalities

Hyper-secretion (usually associated with benign tumour)

Excess secretions increase the blood calcium levels causing kidney stones, bone diseases such as Paget's disease and osteoporosis, due to the breaking down of bone tissue. Any excess calcium may be deposited around organs leading to bone softening. This frequently occurs in post menopausal women, who have a deficiency in the hormone oestrogen. Oestrogen levels suppress parathormone levels usually, so as oestrogen levels decline in post-menopausal years, high levels of parathormone increase the risk of osteoporosis.

Hypo-secretions

With low levels of parathormone, the body is unable to use calcium or even move it around the body therefore insufficient levels of calcium ions reach the skeletal muscles. This affects muscle contractions which results in muscles going into spasm and producing involuntary convulsive contractions and irritability of the nervous system. Also low levels of calcium will lead to sparse, dry and brittle hairgrowth.

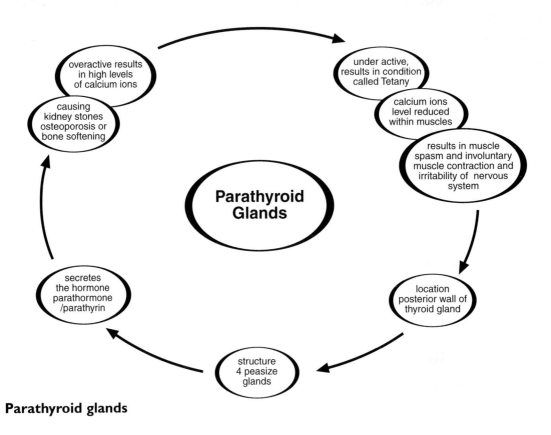

Parathyroid glands

The adrenal glands

Location: There are two small yellowish glands found capping the top of each kidney.

Structure: The adrenal glands are 4cm in length and 3cm in thickness approximately. Each gland is divided into two layers, an outer cortex and inner medulla. The cortex is composed of the same type of tissue as the kidneys and is firm in texture and yellow in colour, whilst the medulla is composed of nervous tissue, the same as the sympathetic nervous cords, and is dark brown in colour. The adrenal glands have a good blood supply from the aorta and renal arteries.

The medulla: Secretes the hormones noradrenaline and adrenaline. Adrenaline causes a chemical chain reaction which increases the sensitivity of the nervous system so that the body responds more rapidly to external stimuli, during moments of shock, fear or excitement. The prickling sensation at the back of the neck, and hairs standing on end, and trembling are all caused by the action of adrenaline. When we experience high levels of adrenaline over a prolonged period of time as with stress, this can lead to unwanted hairgrowth in the male pattern due to stimulation of the adrenal cortex at the same time as the medulla.

Action of adrenaline	Result of adrenaline
Increases heart rate	Raises blood pressure in conjunction with vaso constriction
Heart blood vessels dilate	Increased oxygen to tissues
Blood vessels of skin and gut constrict	Skin goes pale, less blood available to skin, more blood for muscles and brain
Slows down digestion.	Allowing more energy for flight or fight
Glycogen in liver and muscles is converted into glucose	More energy to muscles for rapid response and they tire less easily
Dilation of the bronchioles	Increased oxygen to the lungs so improved respiration
Contraction of spleen	Increases volume of blood circulating
Contraction of arrector pili	Makes hairs stand erect
Pupils dilate	Vision more acute
Hearing becomes more acute.	

Noradrenaline's function is to maintain the body's blood pressure through general vaso-constriction of the body with the exception of the arteries of the heart.

The adrenal cortex

Secretes over 50 adrenal hormones known as steroids, which can be divided into three groups as follows:

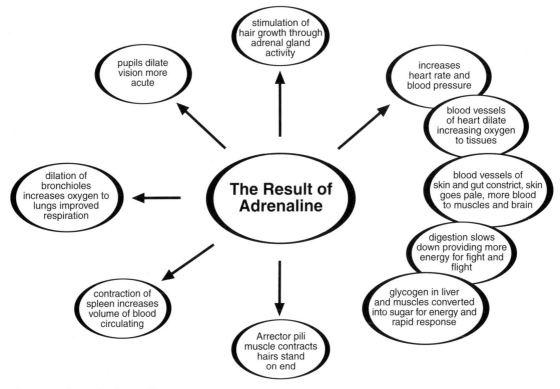

The results of adrenaline

✦ **The sex hormones** These hormones are produced in smaller quantities and supplement the sex hormones produced by either the ovaries or testes. These hormones are primarily concerned with depositing protein in the muscles, and the retention of nitrogen particularly in males.

✦ **Mineralcorticoids** Aldosterone is the main mineralcorticoid and regulates the water and electrolyte balance of the body, which affects blood volume and pressure, by controlling levels of sodium and potassium ions within the body. Aldosterone acts on the kidney tubules and stimulates the reabsorption of sodium ions raising the level within the bloodstream, and decreasing the level of potassium, by excreting it. When sodium levels drop, more aldosterone is secreted stimulating more reabsorption of sodium. This is a finely balanced system and if there is an imbalance it leads to excess fluid being retained leading to oedema/swelling of the tissues.

✦ **Glucocorticoids** Cortisol is the main glucocorticoid and helps regulate the metabolism and is secreted by the adrenal cortex when stimulated by either stress or the pituitary gland secretion of adrenocorticotrophic hormone. It acts on the metabolism to encourage storage of glycogen in the liver and its conversion into glucose for energy within the tissue cells, raising blood sugar levels and stimulating the use of proteins and fats as energy foods when required by the body. Cortisol depresses levels of circulating lymphocytes and lysosomes having an anti-inflammatory action which means wounds take longer to heal. Our body's internal clock is controlled by levels of cortisol. When levels are low, sleep is induced and as levels rise, for example: between 6am and 9am we wake up. After lunch we often feel sleepy because cortisol levels drop initially only to rise by teatime.

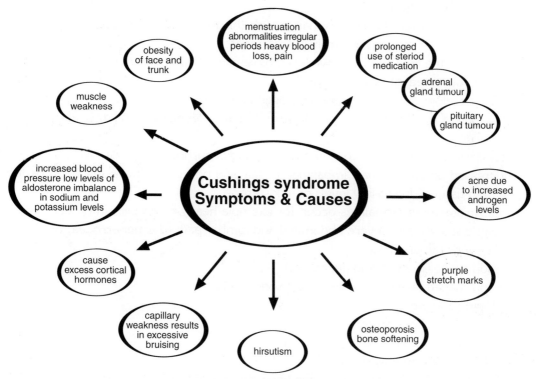

Symptoms and causes of Cushing's syndrome

Adrenal gland abnormalities

Cushing's syndrome

Excess secretions of adrenal cortex hormones namely cortisol, androgens and other glucocorticoid hormones result in this condition. There are three main causes for this condition, they are:

✦ **An adrenal gland tumour:** There is an excess in the secretions of the hormones cortisol and androgen which results in excessive cell tissue growth. Women between 25 and 45 years of age are four times more affected by this condition than by men.

✦ **A pituitary gland tumour:** May lead to over-secretion of adrenocorticotrophic hormone which stimulates excessive adrenal cortex activity and over secretion of steroid hormones (this is the most common cause).

- **Prolonged use of steroid medication:** This is another common cause of this disease. The taking of steroids long-term has a direct influence on the adrenal cortex, in the same way as naturally produced hormones from this area do. Overuse of steroids produces Cushing's syndrome as a side effect, leading to the following symptoms:
  - excess cortical hormones
  - an increase in facial and body hairgrowth (hirsutism) due to excess androgen hormone levels. It requires electrolysis treatment
  - obesity of the face and trunk whilst limbs remain slender (this may be due to proteins being converted into carbohydrates)
  - acne develops due to increased androgen activity
  - thinning of the skin leads to purple stretch marks developing on limbs, abdomen and breasts
  - capillary weakness leads to excessive bruising occurring
  - increased blood pressure, imbalance in salt and potassium levels results in oedema within tissues, due to low levels of aldosterone
  - menstruation abnormalities occur, for example heavy blood loss, infrequent periods (oligomenorrhoea), severe abdominal and lumbar pain (dysmenorrhoea) or absence of periods (amenorrhoea)
  - mood swings, fatigue and depression
  - moon shaped face due to raised cortisone levels
  - thinning and weakness of the muscles
  - osteoporosis, bone softening
  - alopecia, (hair loss occurs) in females
  - florid complexion may occur
  - darkening of the skin tissues on the neck may also occur
  - high levels of blood sugar.

Adrenogenital virilism

Excess secretion of androgen hormones brings about this rare condition. There is a malfunction within the adrenal cortex which causes it to be unable to use the chemical materials needed to make the steroid cortisone. Instead it converts this material into androgens leading to excess levels. When this condition occurs women become more masculine, as follows:
- hirsutism occurs to face and body areas
- there is deepening of the voice
- acne and coarsening of skin texture may occur
- alopecia, baldness often results
- menstrual problems such as absence of periods occur
- body frame alters building up muscle to resemble male frame
- there is breast shrinkage.

Achard-Thier syndrome (the bearded lady)

This is another rare condition which is usually linked with post-menopausal women and combines the symptoms of Cushing's syndrome and adreno virilism syndrome.

Symptoms include:
✧ diabetes mellitus
✧ severe hirsutism of the face (beard)
✧ general obesity
✧ high blood pressure
✧ virilisim, deepening of the voice, receding hairline
✧ acne due to high levels of circulating androgens.

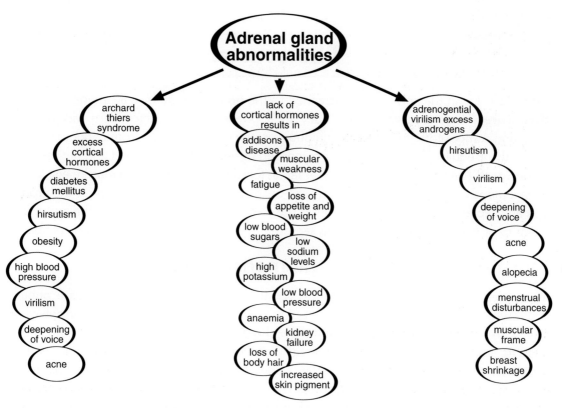

Adrenal gland abnormalities

Addison's disease

Lack of cortical hormones: this condition occurs as a result of insufficient levels of cortical hormones namely androgen, cortisol and aldosterone. It is caused usually through tuberculosis of the adrenal cortex.

The symptoms of the disease are as follows:

✧ muscular weakness and fatigue
✧ weight loss
✧ increased pigmentation of the skin resulting in bronzing effect
✧ lack of blood glucose
✧ high levels of potassium and low levels of sodium, leading to low blood pressure and dehydration through excess water loss
✧ changes in fluid balance leading eventually to kidney failure
✧ loss of appetite
✧ loss of body hair
✧ poor response to stress
✧ anaemia.

The ovaries

Location: Lie in the pelvic cavity attached to the uterus/womb by a ligament.
Structure: There are two ovaries. They are approximately 1cm thick, 2cm wide and 3cm long, and composed of two layers. The outer cortex layer is formed from connective tissue whilst the medulla (the inner layer) is composed of fibrous tissues, blood and nerves.
Functions: The production of ovarian graafian follicles which produce a mature egg (ovum) once a month and secrete the sex hormone oestrogen. The second function is the production and secretion of the sex hormones in the female. Oestrogen, progesterone and a small quantity of the hormone androgen are secreted from the stroma of the ovarian cortex.

Hormones controlling the menstrual cycle

The pituitary gland starts secreting the gonadotrophic hormones to stimulate puberty about two years prior to commencement of the menstrual cycle. These gonadotrophic hormones are nourishing hormones which target the ovaries and stimulate them to function at puberty. The follicle stimulating hormone (FSH) is released by the pituitary gland where it stimulates the graafian follicles within the ovaries to produce an ovum. As the ovum develops within the graafian follicle it secretes the sex hormone oestrogen which increases in amount as the ovum reaches maturity. High levels of oestrogen are detected by the hypothalamus within the bloodstream, which signals the release of the second gonadotrophic hormone the luteining hormone (LH), and results in ovulation. Ovulation is when the mature ripened ovum breaks out of the graafian follicle leaving an empty sac behind, this in turn becomes known as the corpus luteum. It is the corpus luteum which now secretes the second female sex hormone progesterone. High levels of LH inhibit FSH to prevent the graafian follicles producing another ovum, whilst high levels of progesterone are detected in the bloodstream and inhibit secretion of LH.

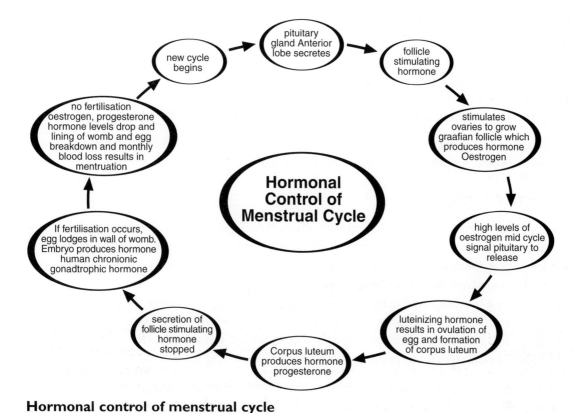

Hormonal control of menstrual cycle

If the ovum becomes fertilized at this stage, it will embed itself into the thickened lining of the uterus, where it will develop into an embryo and secretes the human chorionic gonadotrophic hormone. However if fertilization does not occur, the thickened vascular lining of the uterus starts to degenerate, breaking down and is lost in the menstrual flow.

The actions of the hormone oestrogen

⬦ Initiating and maintaining mature female genitalia and secondary sexual characteristics
⬦ Causes deposits of subcutaneous fat to be laid down and is responsible for the round-ness and width of the female hips
⬦ Reduces the rate of hairgrowth and its diameter
⬦ Inhibits FSH secretions
⬦ Inhibits parathormone
⬦ Antagonistic to androgen hormones
⬦ Reduces sebaceous gland activity
⬦ Stimulates bony growth of pelvis
⬦ Maintains bone density
⬦ Helps prevent heart disease.

Actions of progesterone

✧ The main action is the preparation of the lining of the uterus for implantation and maintenance of pregnancy
✧ During pregnancy prevents ovulation occurring
✧ Stimulates the development of alveoli in the breast.

Androgens are secreted in very small quantities by the ovaries whilst the main secretion of this hormone is controlled by the adrenal cortex.

The menopause

This simply means the finishing of menstruation, which occurs between the ages of 45 and 51 on average, as a result of secretions of oestrogens diminishing and ovulation ceasing. Menstruation becomes progressively more irregular and infrequent and after one year without a menstrual flow the menopause is reached. Whilst this process is occurring there is frequently a hormonal imbalance between the low levels of oestrogen and androgen hormones which often brings about superfluous hairgrowth in the male pattern, usually to the top lip and/or chin areas. This hairgrowth should not be tampered with but treated by an experienced electrologist to prevent the condition becoming severe with time.

Stein-Leventhal syndrome (polycystic ovaries syndrome (PCOS))

This is a disorder which affects the ovaries causing enlargement of the ovaries and the over production of androgen hormones in women during their late 30's and mid 40's generally. With this condition there are usually infertility and menstrual problems as a result of raised levels of the follicle stimulating hormone and the graafian follicles failing to produce a mature ovum (egg). Instead, the ovary thickens because the graafian follicles do not mature and ripen, but becomes trapped and embedded below the surface of the ovary which prevents ovulation occurring. Continued stimulation by FSH leads to an excess of graafian follicles being stimulated and a build up of unripened peasize cysts on the ovaries. Long-term, the ovaries become enlarged, elongated with a pearly white surface, and secrete larger quantities of androgen hormone due to hypersecretion from the stroma of the ovary, which induces unwanted hairgrowth in the male pattern, which will require treatment from an experienced electrologist under medical supervision.

Symptoms of this disorder are:

✧ Hirsutism ranging from mild to severe
✧ Weight problems, for example obesity

✧ Infertility
✧ Menstrual irregularities ranging from absence to infrequent periods
✧ Ovulation failure or irregularity
✧ Enlarged and elongated ovaries.

The Islets of Langerhans

Location: Lie within the pancreas, which is a greyish white organ which lies on the posterior abdominal wall.

Structure: These are a group of specialised cells which are clustered together between the capillaries and the alveoli cells of the pancreas. There are three types of cells, alpha, beta and delta.

Function: The production and secretion of two hormones which regulate the sugar metabolism. These include the hormone insulin from the beta cells, glucagon from the alpha cells, whilst the delta cells produce somatostatin.

   The alpha cells form 25 per cent of the total number of Islets of Langerhans cells and produce the hormone glucagon, which is secreted when there is a fall in the blood sugar

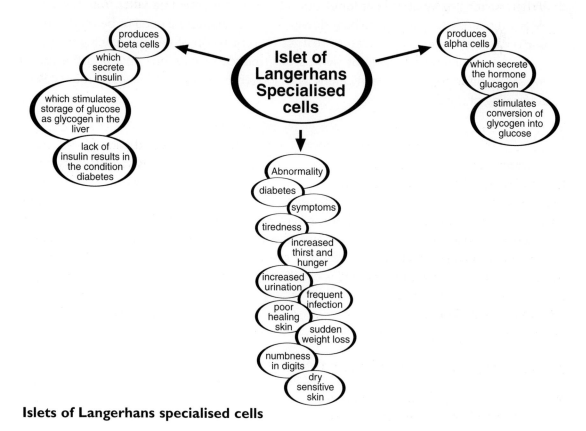

Islets of Langerhans specialised cells

level of the body. Glucagon stimulates the conversion of glycogen (store sugar in the liver) to liquid glucose, there by increasing the blood sugar level.

The beta cells form the remaining 75 per cent of the Islets of Langerhans cells and they secrete the hormone insulin. Insulin is secreted in response to a rise in blood sugar level, for example after eating a meal insulin lowers the blood sugar level thereby stimulating the conversion of glucose (taken in the form of food and drink) to glycogen and its storage in the liver, by increasing cellular uptake of glucose.

Lack of insulin results in the tissues being deprived of nourishment and leads to the body's inability to store glucose, so increasing blood sugar levels and it is excreted into the urine. As the body needs energy and cannot utilize glucose, the body starts breaking down fats and this results in high levels of ketones in the blood, which during the gaseous exchange in the lungs some ketones escape and are exhaled. This can be recognised by the smell of sweet smelling breath as in pear drops or acetone. High levels of ketones may lead to diabetic coma. Therefore the function of glucagon and insulin within the Islets of Langerhans is to regulate and balance the blood sugar. Both of these hormones have an affect on the carbohydrate metabolism, as the metabolism of proteins and fats are closely related to carbohydrate metabolism and that a disturbance in one will affect the others.

When treating a diabetic client for electrolysis extra care must be taken with hygiene as there is a tendency for the skin to heal slowly. The treatment will need to be modified, for example insulated steel needle used to restrict current to tip of needle, spacing of probes further apart to improve healing of skin tissues, reduced treatment time and the use of ozone steaming to promote healing along with longer intervals between treatments again to aid healing of skin.

Pineal gland

Location: Lies in the brain.
Structure: Small pine-shaped gland.
Function: Produces the hormone melatonin during the night and is linked to our body rhythms, for example biological time clock, day and night time, reproductive cycle etc. Jet lag often results when there is a disruption in the secretion of melatonin, due to changes in day and night time rhythms, often a result of travelling long distances. This gland starts to degenerate after the age of seven and is clacified by puberty.

Thymus gland

Location: Lies in the thorax.
Structure: Composed of a densely packed mass of lymphocytes.
Function: Secretes the hormone thymosin which provides stimulus for lymphocyte production.

Student Activity

Complete the following chart with as much information as you can. An example has been done for you.

Name of Gland	Hormones	Effects	Associated Disorders
Adrenal Cortex			
Adrenal Medulla			
Anterior Pituitary	T.S.H. A.C.T.H. Gonadotrophins F.S.H. and L.H. Prolactin Somatotrophin	Controls the menstrual cycle and reproduction	Infertility Polycystic ovaries syndrome
Posterior Pituitary			
Thymus	Thymosin	Simulates antibody production	
Pineal	Melatonin	Affects body rhythms and reproductive cycle	Jet lag
Testes			
Ovaries			
Thyroid			
Parathyroid			
Pancreas islets of Langerhans			

A study of the skin and hair structure | 3

The aim of this chapter is to introduce you to the structure of the skin, hair and appendages. In order to develop your practical skills you will need a good understanding of this subject to enable you to:
- ✧ formulate and adapt a treatment plan according to skin and hair type,
- ✧ recognise the various stages of hairgrowth,
- ✧ adapt your technique to offer the best possible treatment and become a competent electrologist.

The structure of the skin

The skin is the largest organ of the body covering the entire outside of the body. Within 6.45 cm (1 sq inch) of skin there are approximately:
- ✧ 65 hairs
- ✧ 95–100 sebaceous glands
- ✧ 650 sweat glands
- ✧ 17 metres of blood vessels
- ✧ 70 metres of nerves
- ✧ 9,500,000 cells
- ✧ 1,300 nerve endings to record pain.

The thickness of the skin ranges between 0.05mm and 3mm. A vertical section through the skin shows two distinct layers – the outer epidermis layer and the inner dermis layer, these are followed by a subcutaneous fat layer that protects the bones and underlying structures.

The skin is constantly being worn away and replenished by the formation of new cells and varies in density according to the area of the body. It is thinnest on the eye lids and facial lips whilst it is thickest on the soles of the feet and palms of the hands.

The structure of the epidermis

The cells forming the epidermis are composed of stratified epithelium and form five distinct layers. The outer layers are composed of dead and dying cells, due to the keratinization process, whilst the two innermost layers are composed of living cells. It has very few nerves and contains no blood vessels. It is pierced by hair follicles and the ducts of the sweat and sebaceous glands, as well as marked by minute depressions which are caused by the papillae within the dermis. It takes, on average, 30 days for the cells at the base of the epidermis to travel to the surface of the skin.

The stratum corneum

This is the surface layer of skin, consisting of 25 to 30 rows of flattened irregular dead keratinised cells. This layer of skin is a waterproof protective covering, which prevents excessive dehydration of the tissues.

The stratum lucidum

This layer lies below the stratum corneum and is a narrow transparent layer consisting of flattened and closely packed cells, with an indistinct outline and no nuclei. This layer is more pronounced in thick hairless skin, for example on the palms of the hands and soles of the feet.

The stratum granulosum

This is the third layer of the epidermis and is between 1 to 4 cells deep, consisting of flattened clearly defined cells. The keratinocytes begin to break down creating keratohyalin granules in the cell cytoplasm which are a precursor to keratinisation.

The stratum spinosum/prickle cell layer

This layer is 3 to 6 cells deep with nucleated cells that vary in size and shape. The upper portion of this layer is often referred to as the prickle cell layer as these cells interconnect with neighbouring cells. At this stage the cells have a flattened appearance and between the cells are fine intercellular threads which allow the passage of lymph corpuscles.

The stratum germinative/basal layer

Within this layer, cells are one cell deep, rounded and clearly defined with a nucleus and rest on the papillae of the dermis. These epithelial cells are able to divide and reproduce themselves. As these cells form they push themselves up towards the skin surface. Within this layer there are also melanocyte cells which produce the pigment melanin which gives both the hair and skin its colour density. Langerhan cells are also found within this layer and absorb and remove foreign bodies that enter the skin.

The structure of the dermis

This is the largest layer of the skin also known as the true skin. It is composed of areolar connective tissue and contains numerous blood vessels, lymph vessels, nerves, sweat glands, hair follicles, arrector pili muscles and is bathed in water. The dermis has two layers, the papillary and reticular layer.

The papillary layer

This lies directly under the germinative layer and contains small cone-shaped projections called papillae. Some of these papillae contain looped blood capillaries, others contain tactile corpuscles and nerve endings.

The reticular layer

This is the larger of the two layers containing cells called fibroblasts which produce the yellow elastin fibres which make up 4 per cent of connective tissue and give the skin its flexibility. White protein collagen fibres give the skin its strength and make up 75 per cent of connective tissue. Reticulin fibres run between the dermis fibres and structures helping to support them and hold them in situ.

There are also specialised cells within this layer which are called machrophages and mast cells. Machrophages destroy bacteria and tissue debris, whilst mast cells secrete histamin, a substance that enlarges small blood vessels, and heparin, an anti-coagulant that stops the blood clotting. The skin contains sensory nerve endings that run through the dermis, terminating in nerve endings of various types. Branched nerve endings are sensory and found in the hair root and papillary layer, they are sensitive to temperature changes. Other sensory corpuscles include:

✧ Pacinian corpuscles, which are skin receptors within the reticular layer of the dermis that signal changes in pressure
✧ End bulb of Krause, which are minute nerve endings that record the sensation of cold
✧ Ruffini corpuscles, which are receptors in the skin sensitive to heat changes
✧ Meissener's corpuscles, which are found in very sensitive areas of the skin (for example finger tips) and are sensitive to touch
✧ Merkel's discs, which are also touch receptors.

The hair

The number of hair follicles we have are laid down in our genetic make-up, and no new follicles are produced after birth. However, inactive hair follicles may be stimulated to produce hair cells by the hormone androgen.

The total number of hair follicles is equal in both men and women, and it is the activity of the follicles rather than their number that determines the amount of hairgrowth. Hair grows faster during the period between 16 and 46 years of age. Hair density is reduced after 50 years of age, and more follicles are found in the telogen phase, where individual hairs are found to have thickened. More white hair growth occurs or grey hair, which is the

The Hairgrowth Chart

Body Area	% Resting Hairs Telogen	% Growing Hairs Anagen	% Catagen	% Dystrophic or uncertain	% Duration of Telogen	% Duration of Anagen	% Follicles per sq. cm	% Daily Growth rate	Total § of follicles	Approx depth of Terminal anagen follicle
Scalp	13	85	1–2	1–2	3–4 months	2–6 years	350	0.35mm		3–5mm
Eyebrows	90	10			3 months	4–8 weeks		0.16mm		2–2.5mm
Ear	85	15			3 months	4–8 weeks			1 million total for all of head and scalp	
Cheeks	30–50	50–70					880	0.32mm		2–4mm
Beard (chin)	30	70			10 weeks	1 year	500	0.38mm		2–4mm
Moustache (upper lip)	35	65			6 weeks	16 weeks	500			1–2.5mm
Axillae	70	30			3 months	4 months	65	0.3mm		3.5–4.5mm
Trunk							70	0.3mm	425,000	2–4.5mm
Pubic area	70	30			12 weeks	months	70			3.5–4.75mm
Arms	80	20			18 weeks	13 weeks	80	0.3mm	220,000	
Leg and Thighs	80	20			24 weeks	16 weeks	60	0.21mm	370,000	2.5–4mm
Breasts	70	30					65	0.35mm		3–4.5mm

This is a useful guide to the percentage of hairgrowth in various areas of the body, it is not definitive only a guide, more research is still required. Reference R.N. Richards M.D. G.E. Meharg R.N. (Publisher: Arroway)

result of melanocytes no longer present in the follicle or no longer being able to producing melanin.

Hairs grow on most parts of the body, but are always absent from the palms of the hands and soles of the feet, as there are no follicles present. Hairs vary in length, texture and colour depending on which part of the body they grow. Hairs are largely composed of the epidermal protein keratin.

Hairgrowth starts in the epidermis, at the bottom of a long narrow pocket called the follicle, which is lined with epithelial cells. At the bottom of this follicle is a structure called the dermal papilla. It is from this dermal papilla that the cells form the hair. Immediately above the dermal papilla the follicle is quite fat, bulbous and this part is called the hair bulb, and encases the dermal papilla. The rest of the hair within this area is known as the hair root and the part which is visible beyond the skin is called the hair shaft. The hair bulb and the hair root are surrounded by two layers of epithelial cells known as the inner and outer root sheaths. Surrounding these two layers of cells is a layer of the dermis, the papillary layer called the connective tissue sheath.

To the side of each hair follicle is a small muscle called the arrector pili muscle, which when contracted causes the hair to stand erect, away from the skin at an angle causing puckering of the skin known as goose flesh to appear. The hair follicle is fed by a rich localised blood supply which circulates in minute capillaries within the dermal papilla to bring about hair growth, and contains amino acids which help form the protein keratin.

The dermal papilla

Location: lies inside the hair bulb and is the active centre of the matrix region of the hair follicle.

Function: responsible for hairgrowth.

Structure: composed of dermal connective tissue with numerous active fibro blast cells and is concave in shape. It has a permanent capillary in the neuro vascular network, which passes over the bulb of the growing hair follicle and enters the dermal papilla. Most growing follicles contain two capillary loops in the upper part of the dermal papilla region. The number of capillary loops within the dermal papilla changes with the size and shape of the growing hair. A single hair changes drastically in shape and size as it grows and its overall shape and size varies from one cycle to the next, and the pattern of blood vessels in the dermal papilla becomes more complex with successive cycles.

The dermal papilla during the anagen cycle

It is large and attached by a narrow stalk to the basal plate of connective tissue. A basal membrane called the basal lamina separates the dermal papilla from the cells of the hair bulb.

The dermal papilla during the catagen cycle

At the onset of the catagen cycle the basal lamina membrane becomes crinkled up and reabsorbed. The follicle shrinks by one third and the dermal papilla slips its capillary plexus, lying shrunken and isolated just below the follicle.

The dermal papilla during the telogen cycle

During this stage the dermal papilla shrinks again becoming more isolated below the follicle, whilst the capillaries remain intact, but collapsed at the base of the follicle in a tangled mass. When the inactive follicle is reactivated the new hair bulb ploughs down into and through the capillaries and grows inside it. The capillary network from any part of the follicle and sebaceous gland is a continuous system.

The number of dermal cells remains constant. The changes in the size of the dermal papilla are related to the increase and decrease of the size of the capillary plexus feeding it.

Types of hairgrowth

There are only three basic types of hairgrowth:
✧ Lanugo
✧ Vellus
✧ Deep terminal.

Lanugo hair: is found on the foetus and shed usually prior to birth.

Vellus hair: is soft downy fine hair that covers the entire body except for the palms of the hands and soles of the feet. It is normally without a medulla and is about 2 cm long on average. This type of hair grows from the lobe of the sebaceous gland. These hairs never become terminal hairs unless stimulated by topical stimulation as in shaving, plucking etc, systemic stimulation, hormone changes (puberty, pregnancy, menopause), which induce the follicle to grow downwards for terminal hair growth, due to receiving a deep rich blood supply from the dermis. This change may take place gradually over a period of a few months or years. If at an early stage stimulation ceases, the hair will not grow any deeper into the dermis and the replacement hair may even return to its original length.

Vellus hair has a shedding and replacement growth cycle, the same as terminal hair growth, only much slower in rate of growth, often taking two or three months to re-appear and remaining in the telogen stage for six to eight months prior to shedding.

Deep terminal hair: these replace vellus hairs in certain areas during hormone changes in the life cycle, for example puberty, pregnancy and menopause. These hairs are heavily pigmented, coarser in texture and much longer than any other form of hair. They have a well developed root, comprising of a bulb matrix and dermal papilla with a rich blood supply.

A terminal hair has three distinct layers:
✧ the cuticle
✧ the cortex
✧ the medulla.

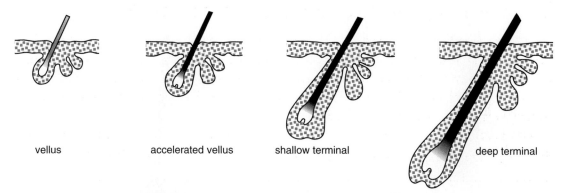

| vellus | accelerated vellus | shallow terminal | deep terminal |

The development of vellus to terminal hairgrowth

The structure of the hair

Cuticle

This is the outer layer of the hair shaft and is composed of a single layer of overlapping clear thin keratinised cells, which adhere to the cortex and are intertwined with the cuticle of the inner root sheath. The cuticle cells are the last cells in the follicle to undergo differentiation. It is surrounded by a thin coating of carbohydrates and fatty lipids that act as a protective film, against the effects of physical and chemical agents.

The function of the cuticle is to give the hair a degree of elasticity, and in conjunction with the inner root sheath help to anchor the hair in the follicle.

Cortex

This is the middle layer of the hair shaft lying between the outer cuticle and medulla. It forms the bulk of the hair shaft and holds trapped pigment granules called melanin which give colour density to the hair. The cortex is composed of several layers of spindle-shaped elongated keratinised cells that are cemented together.

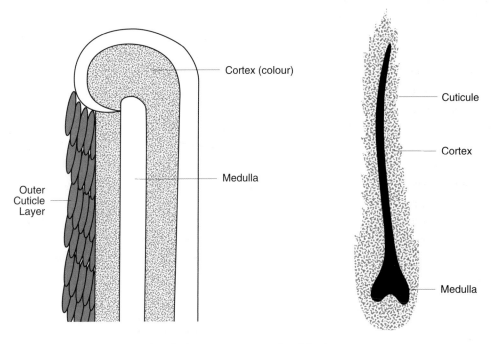

Cross Section of the Hair

- Cortex (colour)
- Medulla
- Outer Cuticle Layer

A Fully Grown Terminal Hair

- Cuticule
- Cortex
- Medulla

Cross section of hair and a fully grown terminal hair

Medulla

This is the inner most layer of the hair and is not always present. It may, or may not, be continuous within the hair, which creates air pockets that are responsible for reflecting light and giving the hair its glossy sheen and colour tones. The cells are composed of loosely connected keratinised cells.

The hair bulb

Location: at the base of the hair follicle where it encases the dermal papilla. It is the thickest part of the hair follicle and is onion-shaped in appearance.

Structure: it has two distinct regions, the upper and lower bulb. Melanocytes are found in the upper bulb just above the dermal papilla.

It is in this lower region of the hair bulb where the matrix cells continuously divide to form new cells, the number of matrix cells is constant, but the number of cells being produced varies. These cells move up from the matrix in rows to enter the upper region of the hair bulb.

In this upper region of the bulb, no mitotic activity occurs. It is here that the cells undergo change and decide to be either inner root sheath cells or cortical cells of the hair-shaft. The cells destined to be inner root sheath cells break away and move out and upwards at a more rapid rate than the cells of the hairshaft. Within this upper region of the hair bulb (above the critical level which is an imaginary line across the widest part of the dermal papilla dividing the bulb into two levels) the keratinisation process starts.

Keratinisation is a process of change that all epidermal cells go through, as they migrate from basal matrix cells to either the stratum corneum or hairshaft. As these cells move up from the basal cell layer of the skin to the granular layer, they synthesise specific con-stituents, for example proteins, and undergo a chemical molecular change, being modified from soft, round gelatinous structures to elongated, hard fibre-like structures, becoming rod-like in appearance and strengthened in structure. As they progress upwards and move through the layers of the epidermis and hairshaft, kerato-hyaline granules are collected at the poles of the nucleus of these cells, which then harden, as their proteins release their water-bound molecules. This causes the cells to dehydrate and harden with the horny cytoplasmic fibrils. Now these cells resemble hair or the surface layer of the epidermis as we know it.

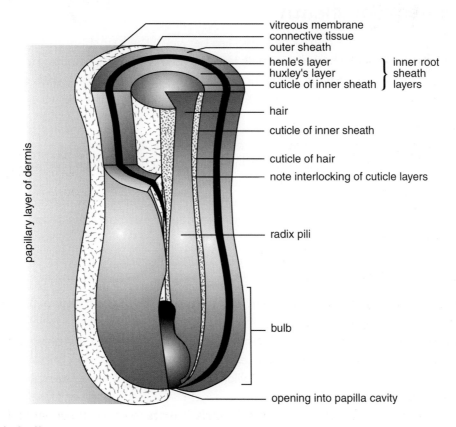

The hair bulb

There are two types of keratin:

- **Pseudo keratin:** or soft keratin which is found in the epidermis, inner root sheath and medulla of the hair. It is supple and pliable with a low sulphur content and a high fluid level and is continuously being shed.
- **Eu keratin:** or hard keratin which is tough, firm and permanent, and never shed. Hard keratin has a high sulphur content with a low fluid level. It is found in the cortex of the hair and nails.

The hair follicle

The hair follicle is composed of the following structures:

- The inner root sheath
- The outer root sheath
- The vitreous membrane
- The connective tissue sheath.

The inner root sheath

Location: arises from the matrix cells and lies between the hair shaft and the outer root sheath. It interlocks with the outer cuticle layer of the hairshaft, originating at the base of the follicle from matrix cells. It grows up inside the hair follicle along with the hairshaft until it reaches the level of the sebaceous gland, then the hair continues to grow up without it.

Structure: composed of germinative epithelial cells and has three layers:

- The outer layer, called Henle's layer which is composed of a single layer of cells, which are in direct contact with the outer root sheath.
- The middle layer, Huxley's layer which is the thickest layer of inner root sheath.
- The inner most layer, the cuticle, which interlocks with the outer cuticle of the hair shaft to help anchor the hair to the follicle.

The outer root sheath

Location: this layer surrounds the inner root sheath, and forms the follicle walls. It is a continuation of the basal germinative layer of the epidermis, which lines the follicle and is continuous with the stratum corneum. Melanocytes are located within this area.

Structure: germinative epithelial cells, capable of reproduction and contains water and glycogen. It is multi-layered in the upper follicle, but its thickness varies being thinner at the bulb region of the follicle.

Function: when stimulated by local blood supply it is the source of the hair germinating cells which in turn leads to the re-building of the lower follicle structure's hair bulb, inner root sheath, etc. It gives support to the follicle. Sometimes it can be felt when trying to probe, it blocks the follicle opening.

The outer root sheath can be divided into three regions:
✧ **The upper region** which lies above the opening duct of the sebaceous gland and is continuous with the stratum corneum of the epidermis.
✧ **The middle region** which extends from the mouth of the sebaceous gland down to the neck of the hair bulb, the cells here are flattened and store large amounts of glycogen.
✧ **The lower region** which surrounds the hair bulb. It is here that the outer root sheath is only two cells thick and slightly elongated. It is in this region that mitotic activity starts when stimulated by local blood supply, hormones and enzymes. There is also a connection here with the cells undergoing keratinisation whilst going through cell differentiation.

The vitreous membrane/basal lamina membrane

Location: this layer separates the outer root sheath from the connective tissue sheath.
Structure: a hyaline non-cellular glossy membrane which results from the degeneration of certain tissues, particularly connective tissue. It has two layers:
✧ **The outer layer** which surrounds the entire follicle and is continuous with the basement membrane of the epidermis.
✧ **The inner layer** which is only found in the lower half of the follicle.

The connective tissue sheath

Location: is a continuation of the papillary layer of the dermis and is connected to the dermal papilla by a narrow stalk. This layer surrounds the follicle and sebaceous gland and is embedded with blood vessels.
Structure: composed of collagenous fibres, some elastic fibres, fibroblasts and macrophages.

The hairgrowth cycle

There are three phases to the growth of a hair follicle:
✧ Anagen (active)
✧ Catagen (changing)
✧ Telogen (tired).

The function of a hair follicle is to produce a hair, when this has occurred the usefulness of the follicle is over and it degenerates, breaks down and lies dormant, resting awaiting stimulation to form a new anagen follicle and a new hair.

Anagen: this is the stage of cellular growth and development. It is the first part in the formation of a new hair and new follicle and involves the complete rebuilding of the lower portion of the follicle. The new structure starts forming from the dermal cord, which is a solid column of epithelial hair germ cells that extend downwards from the base of the remnants of the former telogen follicle, that has previously degenerated and broken down.

The dermal cord begins to enlarge when the cells multiply during mitosis, growing in width and length down into the dermis. At the same time the tip of this dermal cord forms a rounded depression in which the basal dermal papilla cells gather. The structure continues to grow in a downwards direction where the lower part of the cord forms the hair bulb, that in turn encases the dermal papilla. Before the follicle reaches its maximum depth, the matrix cells in the lower part of the bulb are activated to produce new hair cells. They form as the cells move upward from the matrix into the upper hair bulb and begin to differentiate (divide and change) into two distinct types of cells:

✧ The cells of the inner root sheath
✧ The cortical cells of the hair shaft.

The cells continue to move up within the hair bulb and keratinisation occurs in its upper region. The inner root sheath cells move out and upwards breaking away and push their way through the solid cord and form a protective core for the hair to follow. Once the hair

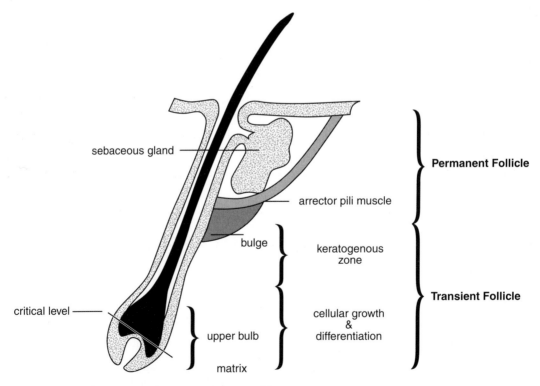

The regions within an anagen follicle

is keratinised it eventually breaks through the apex of the inner root sheath. This occurs about two thirds of the way up the follicle and continues out through the pore as a visible shaft of hair. Throughout this time the follicle continues to extend downwards to the dermis and it is not until the hair has grown to sufficient length above the skin's surface that the follicle reaches its maximum depth and ceases growth. This varies with each individual and each area that hairs grow in. When the follicle is nearing the end of anagen, melanin formation and the formation of the medulla stop simultaneously, the last part of the hair to grow is therefore lighter and non medullated.

The percentage of hairgrowth in this stage varies in each area of the body, generally it is about 88 per cent of hair growth in the scalp region and lasts approximately 2 to 7 years according to each individual genetic trait.

It is only during the anagen phase of the cycle that melanin the colour pigment is produced and transferred to the hair and skin. The melanocytes insert their dendrites into the dermal papilla region and distribute their pigment granules which swell and grow within the cells in this region. An anagen hair, when epilated, has the appearance of being shiny, moist and pigmented. It has a hair bulb, matrix and inner root sheath present, either fully intact or a partially fragment inner root sheath. Anagen hairs are visible 1 to 3 days after shaving or plucking, but after waxing or electrolysis it may take between 2 and 4 months to be visible in the face, thigh and scalp areas according to research by R.N. Richards and G.E. Meharg in USA.

Catagen: this is a transitory, rapidly changing stage of the hair cycle, the complete reversal of anagen. There is approximately 1 per cent of hair in the stage and it lasts for a very short time, about 1 to 2 weeks.

Catagen is the stage where all mitotic activity has ceased in the matrix and no new cells are produced. The cells in the upper region of the hair bulb continue to move up the follicle and differentiate into the hairshaft. The usefulness of the hair follicle is now over and the follicle starts to under go rapid changes. To begin with the basal lamina membrane becomes crinkled up and is slowly reabsorbed. The follicle shrinks by one third of its former size and rises within the epidermis.

Melanocytes in the papilla withdraw their dendites so colour pigment is no longer distributed to the hair. The dermal papilla shrinks and separates and withdraws from the matrix and also rises up within the epidermis. The collapse of the dermal papilla simultaneously triggers the collapse of the hair follicle and the hair bulb, the outer root sheath cells to transform into 2–3 layers of germ cells which surrounds the club hair forming a germinal sac in the area of the lower follicle called the dermal cord, which now resembles a disorganised column of cells at the base of the hair follicle. The hair becomes either detached and is shed or remains lodged in the follicle wall where it drives its nourishment locally and is known as a club hair.

A catagen hair when epilated is dull, dry and shaggy in appearance due to losing water and glycogen. It is partially pigmented in that the root end may appear lighter whilst the tail end is heavily pigmented. This is due to the melanocytes no longer distributing pigment granules.

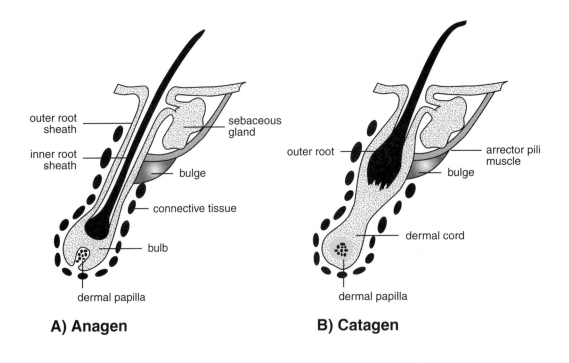

A) Anagen

B) Catagen

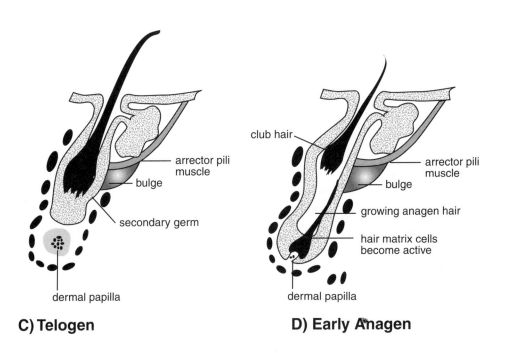

C) Telogen

D) Early Anagen

The life cycle of a hair follicle

Telogen: this is the dormant or resting stage prior to shedding of the hair. We lose between 50 and 150 hairs a day when we comb our hair. The percentage of hairs in this cycle is approximately 11 per cent. This telogen cycle lasts between 3 to 4 months usually in terminal hairs' cycles. The telogen follicle is two thirds shorter than the anagen follicle and continues to degenerate further after the catagen phase. The resting follicle has two distinct regions: the area above the level of the sebaceous gland where the cells are similar to the surface epithelium and the shrunken lower follicle (now called the epithelial sac) where the cells are inactive.

Beneath the follicle the dermal papilla lies greatly shrunken in size as a compact ball of inactive dermal cells and maintains contact with the follicle by means of the epidermal cord. This dermal cord acts in partnership with the inactive dermal papilla and will merge together to build a new follicle when stimulated by the local biochemical processes. The length of time the follicle rests in telogen varies form one area to another and the general characteristics of the individual. However, sometimes the follicle does not rest but is stimulated immediately by the blood supply, hormones and enzymes.

A telogen hair when epilated is a shaft of hair which has a swollen bulb resembling a cotton bud shape and is light in colour and has no matrix or inner root sheath. During puberty the least number of telogen follicles are found, the number of telogen follicles increases after the age of 50 years, resulting in thinning of hair density and increased hair loss.

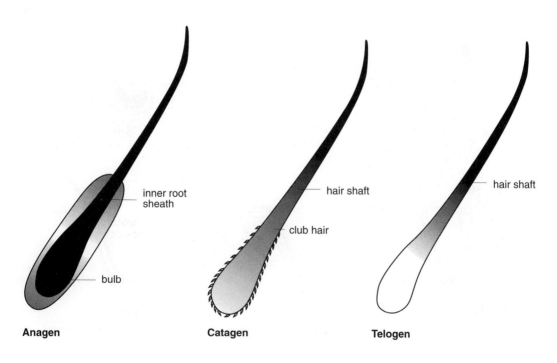

Anagen   Catagen   Telogen

Stages of hairgrowth: appearance of epilated hairs

Unusual hair growth

Lanugo comedones (bundle hairs)

This is a bundle of lanugo hair protruding from a follicle or follicles, resembling a comedone. They are held together by sebum, as they often stem from the sebaceous gland. Usually found in an oily, seborrhoeic skin and can be tweezered from the pore without traction.

Telogen hair that fails to shed

This occurs when a telogen hair that is large in diameter reaches the skin surface and fails to shed. It is usually colourless due to having lost contact with the pigment source after separating from the dermal papilla.

Corkscrew hairs

This is a distorted follicle, very shallow, the bulb lying just below skin surface. They grow from a pilosebaceous unit which has almost been destroyed and has not reformed properly,

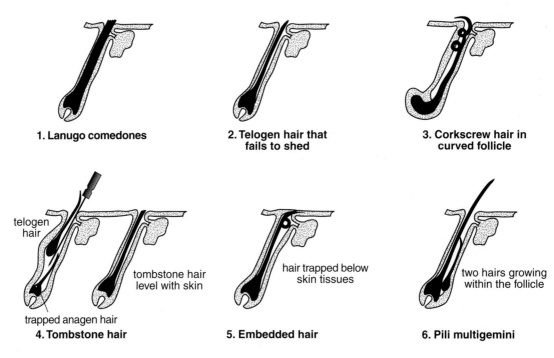

1. Lanugo comedones

2. Telogen hair that fails to shed

3. Corkscrew hair in curved follicle

telogen hair

tombstone hair level with skin

trapped anagen hair

4. Tombstone hair

hair trapped below skin tissues

5. Embedded hair

two hairs growing within the follicle

6. Pili multigemini

Unusual hairgrowth

which can be treated by piercing the skin with a sterile needle and treating the bulb direct. Try to tweezer them out first.

Tombstone hairs

These are remnants of a small anagen hair that has been treated but left in the skin. Sometimes the electrologist will destroy a follicle from which a telogen hair protrudes without realising that a new hair is forming underneath. The tombstone hair becomes a 'foreign body' which works its way to the skin surface. It appears brittle, dull, rumpled, thicker and darker than a normal hair. This hair can be treated by tweezering out or washing and exfoliating the skin.

Embedded hairs

Signs of this are bumps on the skin, erythema, irritation and the hair can sometimes be seen underneath the skin. Caused through dry skin and friction, tight clothing irritating the surface of the skin. To treat this condition you need to pierce the skin with a sterile needle and treat the root, if this is not possible pierce the skin and tweezer hair out.

Pili multigemini

Sometimes called compound hairs. This is caused by a follicle having two or more dermal papilla and results in two or more hairs growing from the same hair follicle. The treatment method is to select the most obvious and treat with current, hopefully the heating pattern produced will affect both hairs, epilate the treated hair and try to remove the second hair if treatment has worked this hair will epilate easily.

Skin types

Oily skin: if the skin is oily, there is usually a higher level of moisture in the lower skin tissues, enabling treatment to be very effective. Sebum acts as an insulator against the current reaching the skin surface layer. Generally this type of skin will have pustules, and papules with enlarged pores, which make insertion easier (and a disturbed pH balance). Care must be taken to prevent infection occurring.

Sensitive skin: this skin type is fine textured with dilated capillaries often present and dry patches. It responds readily to the current with an erythema becoming pronounced. Current intensity will have to be carefully adjusted to suit skin tolerance, spacing of treatment and length of treatment will have to be considered to ensure no adverse reaction occurs. Sensitive skin often responds well to the blend method, particularly when phoresis is applied either before or after treatment.

Dry skin: lacks moisture (dehydrated) which is necessary for the high frequency current to work effectively and therefore current intensity will need to be higher to produce the best possible effect in the treatment area. Needle insertion may be affected by dead epidermal cells blocking the follicle opening. Vapour steaming before treatment may alleviate this problem.

Moist skin: this skin conducts current readily, due to its high level of moisture throughout the layers of the skin. Therefore current intensity needs to be monitored and adapted to prevent current flashing up onto surface tissues, before it has effectively treated the germinative matrix area. The blend method is suitable for this skin type, due to the use of a lower intensity of high frequency current and the galvanic action occurs relatively quickly.

Black skin structure and treatment points

The stratum corneum of the epidermis is much thicker in black skins and the surface tends to desquamate giving a greyish scaly appearance. The scales contain melanin granules, as melanin is present in all five epidermal layers. The number of melanocytes in black skin is approximately the same as in white skin, but the melanin granules secreted are four times larger.

There are more collagen fibres in the dermis of this skin making it very strong. Degeneration of collagen due to ageing is much slower in black skins which retain their elasticity for longer.

The sebaceous glands are also more numerous and a greater proportion open directly onto the skin surface instead of into a hair follicle. The epidermis of black skins absorbs 70 per cent of ultraviolet radiation reaching it, whereas white skins absorb only 25 per cent. However, the heavy pigmentation allows only 5 per cent to pass through it to reach the dermis. In white skin 15 per cent reaches the dermis. The damaging effect of ultraviolet radiation on the deeper tissues is much less in black skin, and skin cancers occur less frequently. The following points will help you when treating black skins with electro-epilation:

✧ This type of skin is often prone to keloid scarring, do a short test treatment to assess healing ability of skin, do not overtreat tissues.

✧ Black skins can also be very sensitive to heat, showing swelling and heat in the area even when erythema is not visible.

✧ Vapour steaming prior to and after treatment helps skin healing and reduces any sensitivity.

✧ The hairshaft is usually flattened and the follicle curved, making it difficult to position the probe accurately.

✧ Use an insulated steel needle to concentrate current to needle tip to reduce surface reaction.

✧ Use a low intensity of high frequency current, preferred method is the blend, which works well on distorted curved follicles, as sodium hydroxide is able to reach curved follicles more effectively.

✧ Ensure stretch is good to aid insertion, and use the correct diameter needle for hair diameter of a longer length needle.

✧ Space probes out one in six, to prevent overheating of tissues due to heat convergence.

✧ There is a risk of overtreating as it is difficult to detect an erythema with this skin type, and black skins can withstand high temperatures, so give shorter treatment sessions.

✧ If hair is infected or inflamed it is better to free the hair, and cut it short to allow skin to heal around it then treat at a later date.

✧ After treatment apply a cold compress of witch hazel gel. When booking next treatment allow sufficient time for healing of tissues to occur.

review**questions**

Q1   State three changes which occur to the dermal papilla during the hairgrowth cycle.

Q2   List four differences between vellus and terminal hairgrowth.

Q3   State at what stage of the hairgrowth cycle the dermal cord is formed.

Q4   Name two sensory corpuscles associated with temperature.

Q5   List the layers of the hairshaft.

Q6   State at what stage of the hairgrowth cycle pigmentation of the haircells occurs.

Q7   State two ways in which the skin type affects electrolysis treatment.

Q8   List four differences between a black and white skin.

Q9   Name the layers of the inner root sheath.

Q10 Which two structures must remain in contact with each other in order for the follicle to regenerate and produce hairgrowth?

Q11 Name the two layers which form the dermis tissue.

Q12 State the name of the protein found in the dermis tissue which is associated with keloid scarring.

Dermatology | 4

This chapter will equip you with the basic knowledge required by the electrologist regarding common skin disorders, diseases and skin conditions, which you are likely to come across when working so closely with the skin tissues and the general public.

Common skin lesions

A lesion is a structural change in the skin tissues either caused by injury or disease. There are two types of lesions, primary and secondary, having knowledge of these conditions enables us to determine if treatment can be given or if medical referral is required.

Primary lesions

Macule: this is a small pigmented area of skin which is the same texture as the skin tissues surrounding it.

Papule: this is a small solid raised pimple which contains no fluid and may later develop into a pustule, if bacteria is present.

Pustule: this is an inflamed hot, red raised area of skin containing pus.

Vesicle: this is a raised area of skin resembling a tiny blister containing clear fluid.

Bulla: this is a larger version of a vesicle.

Cyst/nodule: this is a rounded swelling which lies below and above the surface of the epidermis and contains either fluid or semi-solid matter.

Wheal: this is an itchy swollen white raised area with an erythema background, caused via a histamine reaction, for example an insect bite or hives and may occur sometimes after electro-epilation, lasting up to a few hours.

Tumour: these vary in size and are either an external or internal swelling of the tissues which are either hard or soft in texture and may be any shape.

Secondary lesions

These are lesions which develop in the later stages of disease.

Fissure: this is a deep crack in the epidermis which penetrates down to the dermis exposing it.

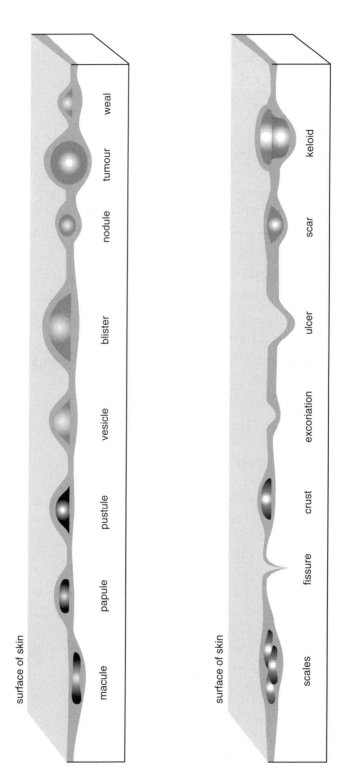

surface of skin

macule   papule   pustule   vesicle   blister   nodule   tumour   weal

surface of skin

scales   fissure   crust   excoriation   ulcer   scar   keloid

Types of skin lesions

Ulcer: this is an open wound which affects both the epidermis and dermis usually accompanied by pus resulting in loss of skin depth and scarring.

Scale: this is an accumulation of epidermal flakes, scales of dry skin, for example psoriasis or dandruff.

Crust: this is the build-up of serum, blood and epidermal cells which dry out to form a scab over a lesion.

Excoriation: this results from friction, scratching or abrasions leaving a raw exposed surface on the epidermis.

Scar: this is tissue which forms, as part of the healing process, at the site of an injury or skin disorder/disease which has penetrated the dermis.

A keloid scar: this is an overgrowth of scar tissue which is caused by overproduction of the protein collagen within the connective tissue and affects appearance of mainly black skins.

Skin disorders and diseases

Skin disorders and diseases may occur as a result of one of the following conditions:
✧ bacterial infection
✧ fungal infection
✧ viral infection
✧ parasite infestations
✧ pigmentation abnormalities
✧ skin cancers
✧ allergens
✧ hereditary factors.

A contagious disease: is a disease which is caught directly or indirectly by contact with an object or person.

An infectious disease: is a disease passed via micro-organisms to other people.

Bacterial infections

Impetigo: an acute highly contagious inflammatory, pustular skin disease, with small red spots that develop into vesicles, blisters then pustules which burst, oozing serum to form honey-coloured crusts. This is caused by bacterial infection, normally *staphylococcus* but may also involve *streptococcus*. Often a secondary infection after chicken pox etc occurring in children and teenagers on face and limbs.

Boil/furuncle: an acute inflammatory condition surrounding a hair follicle, caused by a bacterial infection, for example *staphylococcus aureus*. A boil has a central core of pus and dead epidermal cells, eventually it bursts.

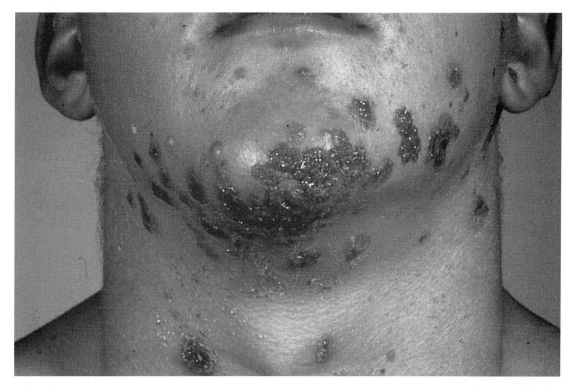

Skin conditions: impetigo

Carbuncle: a group of boils.

Folliculitis: a *staphyloccal* infection similar to a furuncle, except there is a hair protruding from the opening, which appears red and inflamed.

Conjunctivitis: this is highly infectious bacterial infection of the conjunctiva of the eye. There is redness and localised swelling to the eye area with a watery discharge and pus that sticks the eyelids together.

Fungal infections

Ringworm/Tinea: is a highly contagious skin disease which is transmitted through both direct and indirect contact. Fungi transmit disease via spores, the term used to describe these diseases is *tinea*. *Tinea* is characterised by small red patches that form scaly flat rings, and papules or pustules may develop. The effect is one of corrosion on the skin's surface due to a keratin-splitting enzyme action. *Tinea* can affect any area of the body and is named after the area affected, for example: tinea coporis is ringworm of the body, tinea barbae is ringworm of the beard.

Viral infections

Herpes simplex/common cold sore: this is a recurrence of an acute viral infection. Characterized by an itchy sensation, followed by an erythema background with clusters of small weeping blisters. Usually affects the mouth and nasal region and may last from a few days to a week. The virus is spread through physical contact and lies dormant in the trigeminal nerve root ganglion, recurring during periods of stress, illness or with exposure to sunlight.

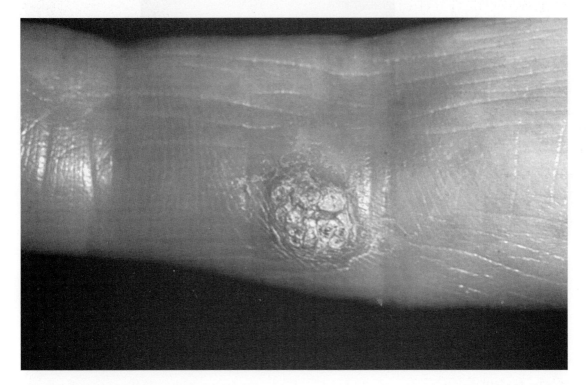

Viral infections: plane wart

Herpes zoster/shingles: this virus is caught after exposure to chicken pox and affects the sensory nerves leading to either the abdomen, chest or face, causing inflammation and small blisters, is extremely painful and may last for months.

Warts: these may be found anywhere on the body. They are a highly contagious viral infection of the epidermis. Varying in shape and size according to the area of the body affected, they are usually firm rounded with either a smooth or rough surface and may be singular or multiple. Types of wart include:

✧ **Verruca vulgaris/common wart:** found on the hands and face.
✧ **Filiform warts:** found on the face.
✧ **Verruca plantaris:** found on the soles of the feet.

Parasitic infestation

Scabies/itch mite: this is a highly contagious disease caused by the scarcoptes scabiei mite and affects the body. The mite burrows under the skin and lays eggs, infesting the skin tissues, leaving grey thread like irregular lines in the skin with papules. This is an extremely itchy condition.

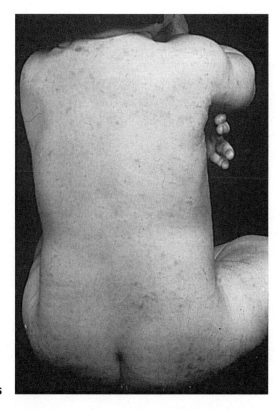

Skin infestations: scabies

Pediculosis/lice: these are small blood sucking parasites which crawl among the hairs, either on the scalp, pubic or body areas. They lay their eggs attaching them to the hair shaft bite the skin sucking the blood, leaving a red mark and creating an irritation, leaving the skin tissues open to secondary infection. Types of lice include:
✧ **Pediculosis capitis/head lice**
✧ **Pediculosis pubis/pubic hair, eyebrows and eyelashes**
✧ **Pediculosis corporis/body hair.**

Non-infectious conditions

Psoriasis: this is chronic skin disease which is thought to have a hereditary and nervous origin, triggered by stress and improves with exposure to sunlight. Usually affects only small areas of the body such as elbows, knees, nape of neck and nail plates, however in extreme cases the whole body may be affected. Psoriasis has the appearance of an erythema background with pinhead size vesicles, dull red lesions with large silvery white overlapping scales. The skin appears very dry and flaky. This condition is due to an over or under production of epidermal cells. Secondary infection may result from constant scratching.

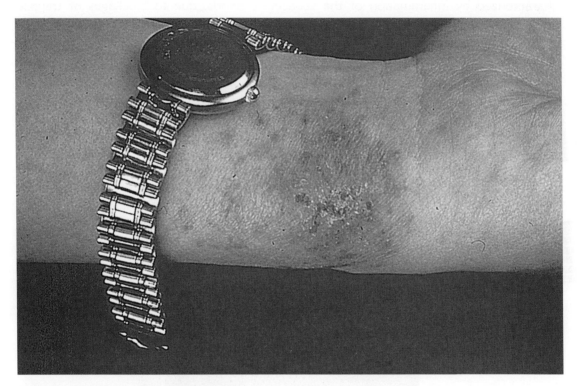

Skin disorders: contact dermatitis

Eczema: this is a condition triggered by an allergic reaction to either an external or internal stimuli and affects 10 per cent of the population. The condition is recognised by general thickening of the skin tissues which results in dry flaky itching, inflamed skin, with papules, and possibly weeping vesicles. This condition may be alleviated by a change in diet in some cases, but is a hereditary condition linked with a fault in the immune system, varying considerably with each individual. There are many forms of eczema.

Dermatitis/contact eczema: this condition is the result of external factors which bring about inflammation of the skin tissues, swelling, redness and vesicles, resulting in very dry, cracked thickened and painful skin tissues. Linked with a single exposure to strong chemicals or the development of a delayed hypersensitivity to a chemical product used regularly in occupational activities, for example Glutaraldehydes, skin cleansers, bactericidal hand washes etc, which do not cause a reaction in everyone. Again there is a hereditary link to suseptibility with this condition.

Sebaceous cysts/wens: an accumulation of sebaceous and epidermal material which lies superficially within the skin, as a smooth, mobile, hard lump which varies in size from a pea to an egg. This condition can be treated by a GP.

Acne vulgaris: this condition is associated with adolescence and overactivity of the sebaceous glands due to hormonal changes. It is more common in males than females. Characterized by inflammation of the sebaceous glands, due to blockages of trapped sebum, which become infected forming pustules and, or boils. The tissues thicken becoming coarse textured with papules, blackheads and milia, and has a yellow greasy appearance. Should be referred to GP if condition severe and infected.

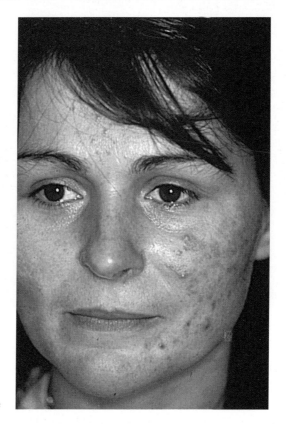

Skin disorders: acne

Acne rosacea: this condition is associated with the thirty-plus age group and is characterized by general redness, dilated capillaries, swelling of the tissues, inflamed papules and pustules, and a coarsening in skin texture, it is usually confined to facial area.

Seborrhoeic warts: these are soft warty greasy pigmented lesions which are found in the elderly. Common sites are face and trunk areas. They vary in colour from brown, grey through to black, with a cleft surface, either oval or circular in shape and may be singular or multiple. They grow rapidly and then stop and are non viral and may be treated by a GP.

Fibroepithelial polyps/papillomas/skin tags: a common skin condition associated with the ageing process. Found usually around the neck and axilla areas. They may be singular

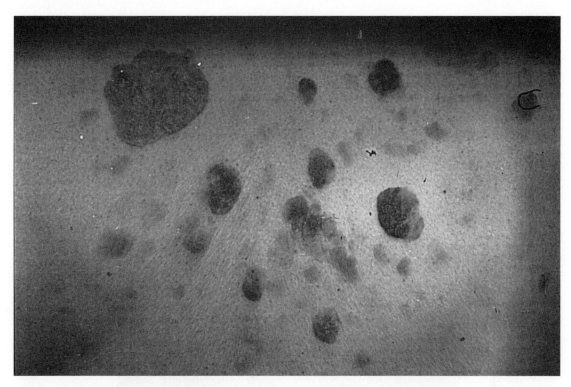

Seborrhoeic warts

or multiple and are a tag of skin resembling a teardrop hanging from the skin surface. A skilled and trained electrolgist may cauterise them for removal.

Hyper keratosis: thickening of the horny layer of skin.

Xanthoma: this skin disorder is caused by a collection of cholesterol under the skin, characterized by the presence of yellow nodules or slightly raised plates in the skin producing yellow discolouration. Common sites are the eyelids, elbows, and knee areas. The patient should be referred to GP as may be linked with a metabolic disease, such as diabetes mellitus.

Pigmentation abnormalities

Hyper-pigmentation: refers to an excess of colour pigment (melanin) in the skin tissues.

Hypo-pigmentation: refers to lack of skin pigmentation.

Leucoderma: refers to abnormally white patches of skin, it may affect localized areas of the body or the entire skin's surface. There are two forms of this condition:

Vitiligo: this is the loss of the colour pigment melanin within the skin tissues in localised areas, forming white patches of skin surrounded by darker pigmented skin tissue. Affecting mainly face, limbs and back areas, found in both children and adults. This condition may be the result of the insufficient levels of the hormones involved in stimulating melanogensis, for example ACTH, oestrogen and progesterone, or that the pigment cells are destroyed by the auto immune system.

Albinism: this is an inherited absence of pigment from the hair, skin and eyes. The skin and hair abnormally white.

Chloasma: associated with pregnancy and the contraceptive pill and refers to patches of darker pigmented skin light brown in colour irregular in shape and size. It is usually located around the eye and upper cheek areas. Fades gradually over a period of time after the pregnancy has terminated, or pill discontinued.

Pigmentation problems: albinism

Solar lentigo/liver spots/age spots: these are large flat patches of hyper-pigmented skin found in the elderly on the back of the hands, forehead and temples.

Capillary haemangioma/portwine stain: consists of a large area of dilated capillaries. The colour may vary from pink to deep purple, usually covers the face and sometimes the neck. This condition occurs at birth and does not regress with time.

Angiomatous naevi/strawberry mark: consists of a small red pigmented area of skin which develops shortly after birth or is present at birth and regresses with time disappearing usually by school age.

Pigmented naevi/moles: these are moles which arise from the pigment-producing cells within the skin. Colour density varies from pink through various shades of brown to black. The shape and size vary from being raised to flat and may be found on any part of the body.

Naevus: refers to an abnormal development of a collection of blood vessels in a localised area. Colour density varies from pink to deep purple.

Halo Naevus: refers to a white patch of skin which develops around a non malignant melanocytic naevus. This condition is more common in adolescents.

Telangiectasia/broken capillaries: these are fine dilated or broken capillaries which vary in colour from pink to deep purple. Most often found between eye and nasal line in upper cheek area. It is associated with hormonal changes, exposure to extremes of temperature and physical trauma.

Telangiectasia angioma/spider naevus: this is a collection of fine dilated capillaries which radiate from a centrally dilated blood vessel, giving the appearance of a spider. Common sites are upper cheek areas, and nasal regions. Cause: see telangiectasia. Telangiectasia may be treated by a experienced electrologist for more details read chapter 12.

Carotenaemia: this condition brings about an orange tinge to the skin colour and is associated with an underactive thyroid gland (myxoedema), it is most obvious on the palms of the hands.

Malignant skin tumours

Malignant melanoma: changes occur in the appearance of a mole, the colour density of the mole deepens usually to blue black and there is an increase in its size and an irregular shape. There may be irritation in the area. Medical referral is essential.

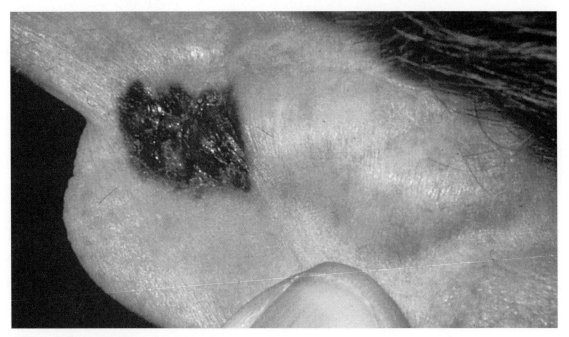

Cancers: malignant melonoma

Squamous cell carcinoma: this is a tumour which arises in the keratinocytes within the squamous epithelium tissue. Common sites are back of hands and lips. It is associated with the elderly and usually more men are affected than women. May be seen as a irregular nodule of skin, that grows rapidly to form an oval or circular raised area which may become ulcerated. Refer to GP.

Basal cell carcinoma/rodent ulcer: this is a slow growing invasive cancerous tumour which penetrates the tissues, eventually destroying the bone. Common sites are between the eye and nasal line and more men are affected by this condition than women. It has the appearance of an inflamed skin tissue with pearly white nodules around raised edges, which irritate and itch whilst not being painful and may bleed easily. Requires urgent GP referral.

StudentActivity

Complete the following chart. A sample has been completed for you.

Disease/Disorder	Cause	Appearance	Treatment
Impetigo	Staphylococcal infection	Oozing lesions forming honey-coloured crusts	Highly contagious. Refer to GP for antibiotic treatment
Eczema			
Herpes simplex (cold sores)			
Sebaceous Cyst			
Squamous cell carcinoma			
Basal cell carcinoma			
Seborrhoeic wart			
Malignant melanoma			
Naevus (mole)			
Spider naevus			
Ringworm			
Psoriasis			

Equipment | 5

The aim of this chapter is to introduce you to a range of basic equipment that the electrologist will need, and the factors which should be considered when making purchasing decisions.

Basic equipment list

Good quality equipment is fundamental to the electrologist being able to perform a high standard of work in comfort, without causing long term injury to herself or the client.

The electrologist must therefore balance the cost of equipment against her health and that of providing a good first class service, which in the long term will generate more business.

Basic equipment required for electro-epilation includes the following:
- The couch
- The stool
- Cold lamp magnifier and trolley
- Forceps/tweezers and needles
- Trolley
- Epilation unit and needle holder
- Needles
- Sharps box
- Waste bin
- Latex gloves
- Sterilising equipment (see chapter 6, Hygiene and Legislation).

The couch

The couch should be of a sturdy construction with a easy to clean surface either vinyl or leather upholstery and well padded for client comfort. It is essential that the couch has an adjustable headrest area and is either hydraulic or electric to allow height adjustability, to enable the electrologist access to any area of the body requiring treatment, and also to enable access for shorter, and less able bodied clients, requiring treatment.

An esthetix flexi height couch

The stool

The stool that you select must reflect your needs. Remember that you will spend your entire working day on this stool and therefore it should be well padded with leather or vinyl upholstery and be wide enough for comfort. It should have a back rest (with lumber support if possible) to ensure good posture, and be adjustable in height to meet your individual requirements.

The cold lamp magnifier

Whatever your age or sight capabilities, this is an essential piece of equipment for any electrologist when performing this type of intensive work, if you want to prevent eye strain and damage. These lamps offer an additional source of light to illuminate the treatment area and magnify even the finest hairgrowth, enabling you to offer a better service, as probing is likely to be more accurate. Also the magnifying lamp acts as a breath shield between you and the client. Ideally this lamp should be on castors to allow for mobility and easy access

Diagram of esthetix multi posture stool

Diagram of esthetix magnifier

to all treatment areas. However there are also available lamps which can be secured to your trolley or wall mounted.

The lamp should be positioned so that the treatment area is clearly lit with the lamp parallel to the area to avoid distortion of hairs, as well as positioned so you can work without knocking the lamp or impeding your probing technique. The light can be used also to highlight and shadow hairgrowth to enable maximum hair removal.

Forceps/tweezers

A small but vital piece of equipment. They come in a variety of different shapes including:
✧ pointed
✧ oblique ended
✧ blunt ended
✧ rounded.

They are usually made of good quality stainless steel and come in varying lengths. Epilation forceps/tweezers should only be used for this purpose otherwise the grip of the forceps is

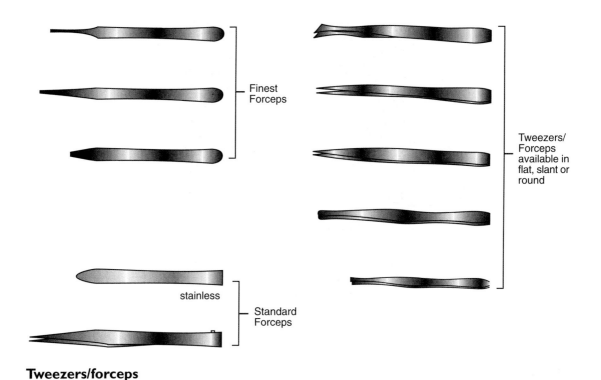

Finest Forceps

Tweezers/ Forceps available in flat, slant or round

stainless

Standard Forceps

Tweezers/forceps

lost and this leads to difficulty in hair removal and reduces speed of treatment. The type of forceps selected is down to personal choice, however they should fit comfortably in your hand and help to improve your general technique. Most electrologists favour one particular style but tend to have a variety of forceps to enable them to remove any hair type and length of hair with ease.

Forceps/tweezers should be kept in the hand or in a sterilising fluid and never left lying on the trolley. A minimum of three pairs are required. One clean ready for use, one sterilising and a spare sterile pair.

Trolley

You will need to purchase a good quality trolley with a wipe clean surface, made of a sturdy construction, on castors, for mobility and easy access to treatment areas. It would be preferably for it to be fitted with an electrical power pack, to prevent trailing of flexes across the salon floor. It should also have two to three shelves to enable storage of all essential equipment close at hand.

Duo trolley

Epilation machines

There are a variety of epilation units available on the market. The choice is personal and usually determined by the range of services you wish to offer. They include the following.

Shortwave diathermy units

These have either finger button control or foot-pedal control, and are manual or automatic. The most popular shortwave diathermy machine at present is the manual finger-button control unit.

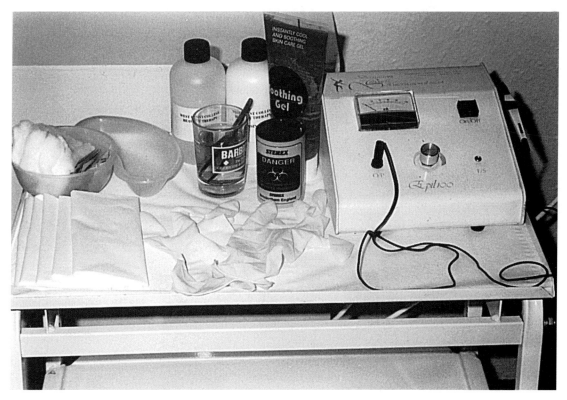

A shortwave diathermy unit

The blend units

This offers three different treatments in one unit. Shortwave diathermy, galvanic and the combination of the two currents. Generally the most popular machine is foot-pedal controlled although some manufacturers offer both foot- and finger-button control options. These machines can be computerised, with timed or manual control according to preference and equipment.

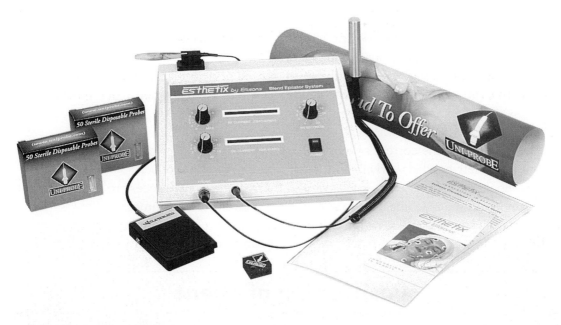

An esthetix clare Blend

Electrodes

The latest design needle holder available on the market is the Probex, needle holder introduced by Ellisons in 2001. This needle probe is easy to load and unload. It has no chuck caps to sterilise and helps to eliminate the risk of cross-infection. It also fits any electrolysis unit. The choice of electrode to go with epilation machines is personal. Some electrologists can only work with finger button control due to their inability to use a foot pedal accurately. You need to try both methods and take your time in selecting your electrode. You must be relaxed and comfortable with it in order to perform the best possible service.

The electrologist's posture

As an electrologist you need to be flexible to achieve good probing technique. The ideal working position should be one that enables you to work in relaxed comfort with easy access to the client, and enable you to work for eight hours without causing fatigue or muscular strain.

If your posture is tense and rigid, particularly in the upper back, neck, shoulders, arms and wrist areas, you will find it difficult to judge the probing depth accurately and the angle of insertion, which may result in a poor technique. Remember, therefore, to try to keep your back straight with the body tilted slightly forward from the hip as required. The working position is seated, standing is generally not acceptable as it leads to poor technique as well as being very tiring and causes bad posture. However, there are some occasions when this might be necessary if you do not have an electric or hydraulic couch or stool and or a client with a respiratory condition who needs to be in a raised position.

Points to remember

✧ Always work on the correct side of the couch – right-handed workers on the left-hand side whilst left-handed workers on the right-hand side of the couch.

✧ You should position machine and trolley so that you have easy access to any treatment area and can see machine dials to adjust current intensity at all times.

✧ Always have easy contact with foot-pedal

✧ Ensure you are within easy reach of all consumable products on trolley.

Positioning of client

The client should be positioned so that she is comfortable and relaxed and so that undue embarrassment is avoided, only expose area to be treated ensuring that the treatment area is accessible to the Electrologist. Leaning on the client during the treatment can be embarrassing and distasteful to the client, as well as uncomfortable, so if it is necessary ensure electrologist does not transfer her body weight. Pillows can be used for extra client support.

Needles

One of the most important pieces of equipment the electrologist has is his/her needles, therefore each needle should be in perfect condition, as the condition of the needle determines the result achieved by the electrologist and the skin reaction of the client.

All needles should be inspected prior to use under an illuminated magnifier, damaged or faulty ones disposed of in a sharps' box. The needle should be of the correct size to enter the follicle, that is the same diameter as the hair. The needle point should be rounded and bright for ease of insertion, a dull old needle will not insert easily or comfortably and if it is too sharp and pointed it will pierce through the follicle wall or its base.

The depth of the hair being treated determines the length of the needle to be used, the needle must be long enough to reach the germinative layer of the hair follicle. Normally the larger diameter hairs and faster-growing hairs are the deepest follicles, whilst the smaller diameter and slow-growing hairs are the most shallow follicles.

Today's needles come in varying lengths, shorter and regular lengths, with regular being the longest. It is safer to select a needle that is too long rather than too short.

Diagram of the varying needle radiation patterns of current

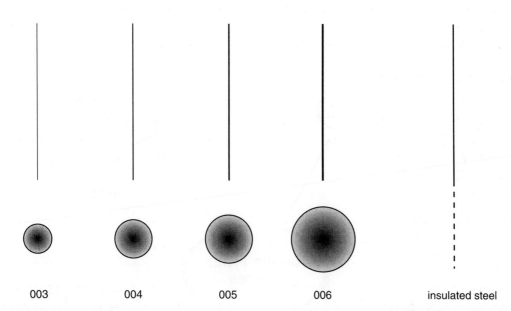

| 003 | 004 | 005 | 006 | insulated steel |

Varying needle radiation patterns of current

The diameter of the needle is determined by the diameter of the hair being treated. It must be remembered that the greater the needle diameter the less intense is the field of current produced and the less pain the client will experience from a given intensity of current, too small a needle diameter increases the current intensity and pain factor for the client.

The use of too large a needle diameter can cause excesive expansion of the follicle, which can break the capilliaries surrounding the follicle and cause black and blue marks – bruising.

Sterex disposable needles (introduced in 1980)

These are a two-piece steel needle similar to the Ferrie needle. They are packed individually in sealed packets and treated by Gamma Irradiation, sterilisation lasts five years from date shown on packet. They are also available in a range of diameters from 003 to 006 and in shorter and regular lengths. This is denoted by S or R after the needle size, for example 3r. All these needles are also available in insulated steel (3I) and gold plate (3G). For treatment of warts and skin tags there is also the 10 needle.

These needles are widely used and considered to be the best method of preventing cross infection, as each client receives a new sterile needle at each visit which is then disposed of according to legislative requirements.

The Ballet needle (introduced 1988)

This is a tapered single one-piece needle of highly polished stainless steel, available in sizes 002 to 006.

They come in prepacked packets having been sterilised by Ethylene Oxide Gas. Also available in 24 carat gold plate and insulated steel.

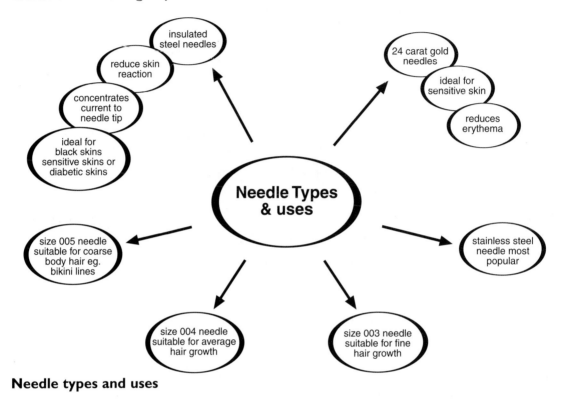

Needle types and uses

The Carlton needle (introduced in 1989)

This is a two-piece flexible needle of polished stainless steel, again these needles come in prepacked sterilised packets, which have been treated by Gamma Irradiation.
Also available in sizes 003 to 006, (similar to the sterex needle).

Ferrie needle (two-piece straight needle)

These are fine needles set into a large base shank and come in a range of diameters from 003 to 006. They were widely used until the invention of the disposable needle. They are a very durable needle and combine flexibility and strength.

Insulated steel needle

First introduced by the Germans, a very long and flexible needle, available originally in only one size, and a much thicker needle due to being covered with an insulated material which left 1/8 inch exposed. Probing was often difficult with these needles.

However today's modern insulated needles are much improved, finer with a modern polymer insulation material which does not hinder insertion into the follicle. These needles are ideal for sensitive, diabetic or Afro-Caribbean skins, as they concentrate the current to the tip of the needle, reducing surface skin reaction and the field of current radiation. Ideal for the flash method.

Platinum needles

Have no base shank and are very fragile needles with a short lifespan and are not suitable for the trainee.

Gold plated needles

A gold plated needle consists of a stainless steel needle which has a 24 carat gold plate bonded to its surface. This needle is ideal for sensitive skins as it reduces swelling and erythema. It has a slippery surface which aids insertion into the follicle. Gold is a good conductor of electricity.

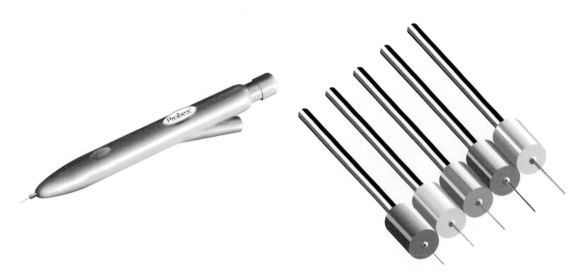

A probex needle and needle holder

Uni probe

This is a disposable pre-sterilised probe with a protective cap, made of stainless steel, which eliminates the need for a chuck cap. It is slender (to increase the field of vision) and colour coded to denote size. Available in sizes 002 to 006. The uni probe eliminates the risk of needle to cap to client contamination.

Probex

This consists of two disposable surgical steel needles, which are colour coded according to size and available in sizes P2 to P6.

Sharps box: this is used for all contaminated epilation needles or medical syringes, etc.

Waste bin: this should ideally be a pedal bin, to reduce chance of cross-contamination.

Latex disposable gloves: a new pair is required for each treatment, to protect the electrologist, and reduce the risk of cross-infection.

reviewquestions

Q1 State why all electrologists should use a cold lamp magnifying lamp?

Q2 List one reason why it is advisable to have a selection of forceps/tweezers shapes.

Q3 Identify what needle type is the best choice for a client with a sensitive diabetic skin, with fine shallow hairgrowth.

Q4 Name the year that the first pre-packed sterilised needle was introduced and by whom?

Q5 State what two factors determine needle diameter?

Q6 Explain the possible reaction that could result when needle choice is too large.

Q7 Identify which needle diameter produces the more intense heating pattern – a 003 or 004?

Q8 State two factors which need considering when purchasing either a stool or couch for electrolysis treatment?

Q9 Briefly explain why good quality equipment is important.

Q10 Name the new type of needle available which prevents cross infection via the needle cap.

Q11 List two types of electrodes.

Q12 Name two factors which determine the choice of epilation unit.

Hygiene and Legislation | 6

This chapter introduces you to hygiene procedures and the reasons why we need to observe them. Always remember electrolysis is an invasive procedure and, therefore, carries more risks than most of cross infection. This chapter also informs you of legislation applicable to electrolysis to keep you fully informed as a professional.

Why we sterilise

There has been much public concern regarding epilation over the years, as it is an invasive treatment. There is a greater risk of cross infection occurring due to the treated hair follicle being an open wound, susceptible to infection. It is, therefore, essential that all electrologists realise the importance of embedding hygiene procedures into their daily activities.

The electrologist needs to fully understand the legislation applicable to electrolysis and the beauty industry and fully integrate it within their daily routine to ensure that they maintain health and safety, minimising the risk of cross infection as well as meeting their legal and professional responsibilities to the industry and the general public. Electrologists could find themselves in breach of one of the many pieces of legislation applicable and at risk of losing both their reputation and business if they do not comply with current legislation.

The electrologist has a moral and legal obligation to ensure the following:

✧ That they reduce the risk of cross infection and the spread of diseases such as Hepatitis B etc, to their employees and clients as well as themselves

✧ Legislation also requires that the electrologist takes every precaution to reduce or prevent cross infection occurring, for example carrying out sterilisation and hygiene procedures as required by legislation. The local government bye-laws (Miscellaneous Act 1982), are monitored by the local Council's Environmental Health Officers, who have the power to impose large financial fines and to enforce salon closure if hygiene and safety standards do not comply with the bye-laws and Health and Safety at Work Act 1974

✧ The Health and Safety at Work Act 1974 must be considered along with the Health and Beauty Industry Code of Practice and the Code of Ethics of specific professional bodies, for example The Institute of Electrolysis etc

✧ Another consideration is that in the event of a client suing for compensation due to contracting an infection, you would need to prove that your hygiene procedures are in line with legislative requirements and that you have taken every precaution to minimise the risk of cross-infection resulting from treatment within your salon.

Personal Hygiene

As a professional electrologist it is essential that you have the right image to present to the general public as first impressions influence the client's perception of the standard of professionalism being offered. You must therefore develop and maintain a high standard of both salon and personal hygiene, as well as being well groomed at all times.

The electrologist should ensure that:
✧ They take either a daily bath or shower and use an anti-perspirant deodorant, to prevent body odour.
✧ Brush their teeth regularly and use a mouthwash, particularly if a smoker or eating strong flavoured food. Electrologists work in close proximity to the client, particularly when working on facial areas, and it is unpleasant and offensive to the client if your breath carries an odour.
✧ A clean freshly laundered overall should be worn daily.
✧ Finger nails should be scrubbed clean, kept short and free of nail enamel, no jewellery other than wedding ring should be worn, due to the risk of bacteria lying within facets of gems.
✧ Any open wounds or abrasions should be covered with a plaster to prevent spread of infection, and disposable gloves worn.
✧ No smoking or food and drink should be consumed within the treatment area, to comply with legislation.
✧ Electrologists should have the Hepatitis B vaccination to prevent them being at risk of contracting this disease. Electrologists are at a greater risk than some health workers coming into direct contact with body fluids, because electrolysis is an invasive treatment.
✧ Most electrolgists or therapists wear a standard white uniform dress or white tunic with navy or white trousers or skirt.
✧ Hair should be clean, washed frequently and tied off the face to prevent impeding the probing technique or trailing over the client.
✧ Footwear should be low heeled to help posture and fully enclosed to meet health and safety requirements. In the event of spillage of chemicals or dropping instruments on feet, injury may result if incorrect footwear is worn.

Terminology

Sterilisation: refers to the destruction of all living organisms and their spores, preventing bacteria from reproducing.

Disinfectants/bactericides: refer to chemicals which are used to prepare treatment areas making them favourable to health by destroying bacteria, however they tend to leave the spores of bacteria behind and therefore bacteria will reproduce and all surfaces will need to be continuously prepared with these solutions.

Antiseptics/bacteriostats: refer to chemicals which only inhibit or limit the growth of bacteria.

Virucide/Biocide/Fungicide/Sporicide: refer to chemicals which destroy either viruses, fungi or spores and a biocide is a sterilising agent as it destroys all bacteria and their spores.

Asepsis: refers to the state of being free from pathogenic organisms – harmful germs.

Sepsis: refers to the state of being infected with pus-producing organisms.

Antisepsis: refers to the prevention of sepsis through good hygiene procedures.

Pre-sterilisation

Before being able to decide on any method of sterilisation for equipment, we must first clean all tools physically by scrubbing them in hot soapy water and a disinfectant solution, for the following reasons:

✧ To remove any organic material from the tools, such as skin and hair from the previous client, and microbes which are invisible to the naked eye which often become trapped within grooves of forceps/tweezers.

✧ The cleaning process reduces the amount of contaminated material on the tools which means sterilisation will be more effective when carried out.

✧ Any grease on the tools will have been removed and will therefore not prevent sterilisation from being achieved.

✧ Regular pre-cleaning of tools prior to sterilisation prevents an impenetrable film of organic matter from building up on tools.

Methods of Sterilisation

Methods include:
✧ the Autoclave – moist heat sterilisation
✧ radiation – gamma radiation
✧ gas – ethylene oxide
✧ Glass Bead Steriliser.

The Autoclave

This is the most widely used and recommended method of sterilisation. It is really just a sophisticated pressure cooker, which is a quick and efficient method of sterilisation for small tools such as forceps/tweezers for the electrologist. The autoclave works when distilled water is placed in the reservoir and the lid closed. The operator presses the start button triggering an automatic sterilising cycle. The water is heated until it boils under pressure and the temperature is 126° centigrade and maintained for about 20 minutes to ensure the destruction of all germs. The steam is expelled at the end of the sterilising cycle, to relieve the pressure. This is monitored by a sequence of colour coded lights which show the progress of the cycle.

Special paper strips can be used to confirm sterilisation has been achieved when using the autoclave. They have a colour coded dot which changes from yellow to purple once the desired temperature has been achieved for the correct duration. (Each autoclave sterilisation treatment time will vary with manufacturer).

Ideally if you cannot sterilise a piece of equipment in the autoclave you should use disposable products such as disposable chuck caps to minimise risk of cross infection.

Radiation

This method of sterilisation uses non-ionising radiation gamma rays or high electrons. Gamma irradiation using an radioscope source such as Cobalt 60 is widely used to sterilise pre-packed electrolysis needles. The packet has a colour change indicator which confirms sterilisation conditions have been achieved, as well as a 'use by date'.

Gas

Ethylene oxide gas is used to sterilise some pre-packed sterilised electrolysis needles. The sterilising chamber reaches temperatures ranging between 20–55 centigrade then filtered air is used to removed any gas residue.

The Glass Bead Steriliser

This method is used only for very small tools such as electrolysis needles or forceps/tweezers and is no longer widely used, since the invention of pre-packed sterilised disposable needles and the wide availability of autoclaves. These sterilisers consist of an electrically heated box surrounded by a protective, insulated case, containing one or more chambers filled with tiny glass beads which are heated to around 250° centigrade to achieve sterilisation. The glass beads heat up and transfer the heat by conduction to the tools.

The disadvantage of this method of sterilisation is that needles or tweezers could not be fully immersed within the steriliser and therefore one part of the object remains unsterilised.

A

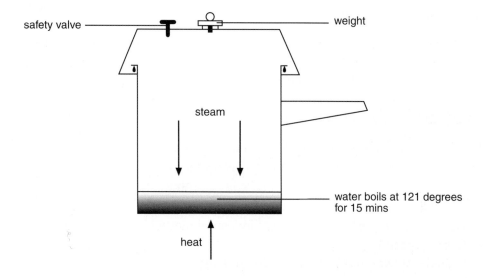

safety valve — weight

steam

water boils at 121 degrees for 15 mins

heat

B

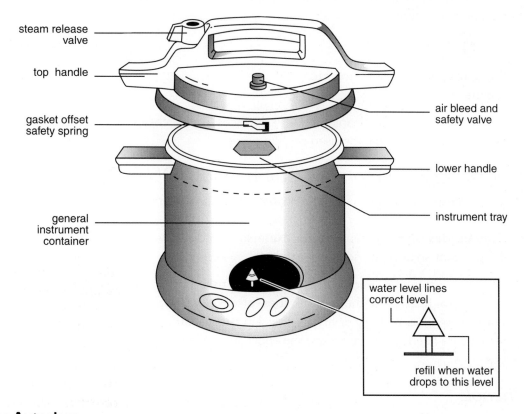

steam release valve

top handle

gasket offset safety spring

general instrument container

air bleed and safety valve

lower handle

instrument tray

water level lines correct level

refill when water drops to this level

The Autoclave

Incineration

Used to destroy needles and contaminated waste, which have been stored in yellow hazard waste bags and sharps boxes. Organised collections for incineration can be arranged through your local refuse collection services.

Wet Sterilisation

This occurs when we wash work surfaces, floors etc with chemical disinfectant solutions to reduce or destroy pathogenic micro-organisms.

Alcohol

✦ **Isoproply alcohol**: is a mixture of industrial methylated spirit and castor oil
✦ **Ethyl alcohol**
✦ **Industrial Methylated spirit:** 70 per cent
✦ **Surgical spirit**.

All of the above alcohols are suitable for cleaning items such as needle holders and trolleys etc. Isoproply (70% alcohol) is also used for wiping the skin tissues prior to treatment and is the main ingredient in mediswabs.

Halogens

✦ **Chlorine:** domestos, milton etc.
✦ **Iodine**

Chlorines can be used for cleaning of work surfaces, floors, chairs, stools, couches and non-metallic objects. Iodine can be used on skin tissues.

Quaternary Ammonium Compounds (QUACA)

✦ **Cetrimides:** used for cleaning skin tissues or protecting them, for example Savlon cream.
✦ **Diguamides**: skin disinfectants for example chlorhexidine, hibiscrub etc which contain 0.5 per cent solution of isoproply alcohol.

All of the above can be used directly on the skin tissues to sterilise hands prior to treating clients, or to help heal the skin tissues after electrolysis treatment. However the Diguamides tend to be very drying to the skin tissues, stripping them of their natural oils, therefore care needs to be taken and the application of a hand cream daily to rehydrate skin tissues.

Phenols

Phenols include Dettol and Dettox, which are used to clean work surfaces only.

Aldehydes

Formaldehyde: no longer used as it is unsafe.

Glutaraldehyde: Cidex, Sporicidin, Totacide and Asep. Glutaraldehydes are strong chemicals which are known as skin irritants, capable of irritating the operator's eyes, throat and lungs. Great care must be taken to ensure that inhalation of vapours and contact with the skin tissues does not occur. These chemicals should therefore be used with caution and handled only where there is good ventilation and when wearing protective gloves, apron and eye protection, as well as stored under COSHH regulations.

Active glutaraldehyde solution of 2 per cent is a chemical disinfectant ideally suited for small tools which cannot be heat sterilised, such as plastic chuck caps or can be used to store tools in after the autoclave to keep sterile, for example tweezers. However tools should then be rinsed in water to remove all trace of chemicals.

Cidex: consists of two solutions, a bottle of blue activator is added to a litre of clear cidex solution. Once the solutions mix together they are active with a life span of 14 or 28 days according to type.

Until recently these chemicals have been widely used in both the beauty therapy and medical fields, however the medical field is phasing out gluteraldehydes, replacing them with alternative chemical solutions. Advice should be sought from a local Environmental Health Officer on its suitability of use, or alternative solutions.

Sporicidin: similar to Cidex it consists of two solutions of 1 per cent which is mixed to form an active solution. Again use is not recommended due to causing severe skin reactions.

Salon Hygiene and good practice

At the start of your day you should ensure that the following occurs:

✧ All trolley surfaces, magnifying lamps, epilation units, flexes and needle holders are wiped over with an alcohol based product, for example isopropyl alcohol or surgical spirit.

✧ Each covered pedal bin must be lined with a disposable liner.

✧ All equipment to be used must be sterilised in an autoclave before and after each client to reduce risk of cross infection. You should, therefore, have an abundant supply of tweezers/forceps, chuck caps etc.

✧ If using linen, towels, or supports they should be laundered after each client.

✧ There should be a supply of disposable tissue paper available, which is changed after each client.

✧ A range of pre-packed sterilised disposable needles in a variety of types, lengths and sizes should be available.

✧ Ventilation and heating should be adequate to ensure that there is a fresh supply of circulating air to prevent discomfort.

❖ That all floors, work surfaces and couches have been cleaned with a chlorine based product (for example bleach, or milton) diluted in hot water as per manufacturers guidelines.

Client preparation should be as follows:
❖ Consultation to establish treatment needs (see chapter 7)
❖ Wash your hands before and after each client with anti-bactericidal handwash and dry, then wear latex disposable gloves
❖ Cleanse skin tissues with cleansing milk to remove traces of make-up without clogging pores
❖ Tone off skin tissues
❖ Wipe skin tissues over with a antiseptic solution such as isopropyl alcohol, to prepare the tissues for treatment
❖ Carry out treatment
❖ On completion of treatment, discharge contaminated needle in sharps box
❖ Dispose of waste in sealed double bin sack.

Treatment of blood spots

As there is a risk of cross infection, if you draw blood when probing it is advisable to carry out the following hygiene procedures:
❖ Wipe the affected skin tissues with dry cotton wool and dispose of it in yellow hazard bag and seal. Loosen the chuck cap and discharge contaminated needle into sharps box carefully, as blood is present on the needle tip
❖ Wash your hands
❖ Insert new disposable needle into electrode and re-commence treatment.

Micro-organisms

Viruses: Are invasive organisms, smaller than bacteria, which vary in shape consisting of an outer protein shell which contains either Ribonucleic acid (RNA or DNA), and are capable of invading a host cell and multiplying, eventually destroying the host cell.

Viruses can only be seen by an electron microscope and are airborne or spread via insects. They spread easily through coughing, sneezing and sharing of body fluids etc, examples of viruses would be:
❖ common cold
❖ influenza
❖ herpes
❖ HIV
❖ hepatitis.

Bacteria: These are single cell organisms without a nucleus, which reproduce by binary fission (dividing in twos). They vary in shape and size according to type. Bacteria can be either harmful (pathogenic) causing infections such as sore throats or harmless (non-pathogenic), for example bacteria in the intestine produce vitamin B2.

Bacteria are classified according to their shape as follows:

✧ **Cocci:** which are spherical in shape of which there are three types:
  ✧ **Staphylococci**: Cluster formations resembling bunches of grapes, responsible for bacterial infections such as Boils and Impetigo
  ✧ **Streptococci:** Chain formations, responsible for bacterial infections such as Tonsillitis
  ✧ **Diplococci:** Arranged in pair formation and responsible for infections such as Pneumonia
✧ **Bacilli:** Are rod-shaped bacteria responsible for diseases such as Tuberculosis and Diphtheria
✧ **Spirochetes:** Are spiral in shape and responsible for the disease known as Syphilis
✧ Bacteria require warmth, moisture and oxygen for growth.

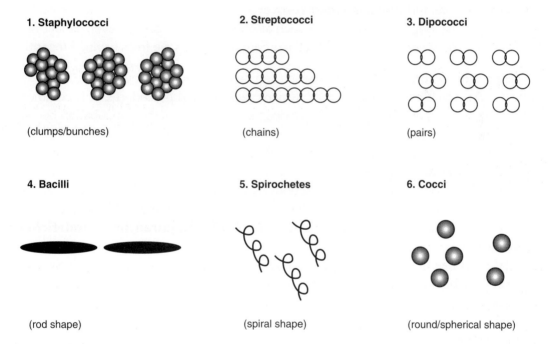

1. Staphylococci

(clumps/bunches)

2. Streptococci

(chains)

3. Dipococci

(pairs)

4. Bacilli

(rod shape)

5. Spirochetes

(spiral shape)

6. Cocci

(round/spherical shape)

Types of bacteria

Viral Infections

Hepatitis B: A highly infectious condition which affects the liver causing it to become inflamed. Hepatitis is spread by human contact, through skin abrasions, body fluids, saliva and blood, even a few drops of contaminated blood are enough to infect you. The incubation period of this virus is between 2 and 6 weeks, with initial symptoms being similar to influenza followed then by:

❖ jaundice, yellowing of skin tone and whites of eyes.
❖ high temperature.
❖ abdominal pains often severe.
❖ loss of appetite.
❖ liver tenderness.
❖ vomiting or nausea.
❖ dark urine.

This virus is extremely hard to destroy being capable of living outside the body for long periods of time – even years. It can only be destroyed by heat sterilisation using high temperatures, for example autoclave temperatures or incineration. Therefore electrologists and Beauty Therapists are at great risk from this virus due to the nature of their work as invasive and the therapist in close contact with the general public. They should protect themselves by requesting immunization against this disease.

Most people infected with this disease recover after a long period of convalescence, however, there may be long term side effects such as chronic liver disease or even cancer of the liver. Each year between 5 per cent and 20 per cent of patients die from having Hepatitis B.

There are other forms of Hepatitis which can be classified as follows:

Hepatitis A: which occurs due to poor hygiene facilities and procedures. It is common in third world countries or wherever there are open sewers. It has a short incubation period of approximately 3 to 5 weeks and generally causes no long term damage to the liver. The death rate from this disease is far less than Hepatitis B being approximately 0.1 per cent annually.

Hepatitis non-A and non-B: Caused by a virus which is neither A nor B, but may produce similar symptoms to these two infections. It is contracted by infected blood and contaminated water or food and has an incubation period of between 5 to 10 weeks.

HIV (Human Immunodeficiency Virus) and AIDS (Acquired Immunodeficiency Syndrome):
The HIV virus has only been around since 1981 approximately and was first linked with homosexuality, however during the 1990's it had its biggest growth rate within the heterosexual population. It can be transmitted via either:

❖ sexual intercourse
❖ blood and body fluids
❖ breast feeding
❖ needle sharing.

To date there is no cure for either of these diseases, although a cocktail of drugs taken daily can manage these conditions. HIV can be present within the body for a number of years without any symptoms developing and not all HIV sufferers go on to develop Aids.

Aids: This disease initially suppresses the body's immune system before eventually destroying it, leaving the body vulnerable to a variety of infection, that are beyond its ability to fight off. This virus targets the 'T lymphocyte helper cells' which are part of the body's defence system against infection by producing anti-bodies. These 'T cells' are invaded by the Aids virus, which is able to convert them into virus manufacturing cells which destroy other cells. Eventually the sufferer dies from a variety of related conditions due to having no immunity to infection, for example pneumonia and heart failure.

Fungi: Are plant structures that do not contain chlorophyll, and therefore are not green in colour and do not require sunlight for growth. They feed on live tissue or dead remains of plants and animals causing decay and diseases such as:

✧ Ringworm
✧ Athlete's foot.

Fungi reproduce by producing spores and there are two types of fungi commonly:

1 **Yeast:** Which includes infections such as Thrush.
2 **Filamentous:** Which includes moulds and mildews.

Legislation applicable to Electrolysis

Whether we are employers or employees, we have a legal obligation to ensure that our actions, or neligence, do not cause others to be at risk. Electrologists should, therefore, have a broad knowledge of all applicable legislation and hygiene procedures, and incorporate this knowledge into their daily practice, thus demonstrating a high degree of professionalism. This will help to ensure that a safe working environment is maintained, good quality services performed, good working relationships generated between the employer, employees and clients. However, remember legislation changes regularly and that whether you are an employer or employee you should keep abreast of these changes to safeguard yourself. To keep informed of legislative changes you need to either contact the local council authority, who will supply you with relevant information, or belong to a professional body and subscribe to professional magazines who generally inform their members of any changes that will have implications for them.

The Health and Safety At Work Act 1974 (HASAWA)

(Superseded Offices, Shops and Railways Act of 1963)

This Act lays down both the responsibilities of the employer and the employee as follows:

The employers' responsibilities include:

✧ Having a duty to care as far as possible for the health, safety and welfare of their employees, members of the public and contractors or those affected by any work the clinic/salon has carried out.
✧ Ensure that all equipment meets health and safety standards and is regularly checked and serviced by a qualified electrician or an appropriately qualified person according to type of equipment being used within clinic/salon.

✧ Carry out regular risk assessments, for example to ensure correct procedures in place to limit risks, such as toxic fumes, and improve staff awareness.

✧ Provide adequate training to ensure that all staff have a working knowledge of and information on safe methods of working practices and safety procedures, for example regular training provided and emergency evacuation procedures in place. The Health and Safety Executive (HSE) produce a guidance poster to the laws on health and safety, all employers are legally obliged to display this poster within the work place.

The employees' responsibilities include:

✧ Employees must follow the clinic/salon rules and regulations regarding safety and safe working practices at all times.

✧ Taking adequate care to avoid endangering the health, safety and welfare of both others and themselves, (for instance mop up spillages as they occur).

✧ Attending staff training provided on health, safety etc and co-operate in all matters regarding health and safety.

✧ Employees must not misuse or interfere with any items provided to protect theirs or others health and safety, for example disposable needles – use only once and place in the sharps bin.

Control Of Substances Hazardous To Health Regulations (COSHH)

These regulations requires employers to carry out regular risk assessments, which itemise all substances used in the clinic/salon or sold to the clients which may be hazardous to health, which may cause irritation, allergic reactions, give off toxic fumes, burn the skin or have flammable vapours etc. Having established this information, the employer must either find alternative less hazardous products for use, or organise safe working procedures which limit the risk of danger, ie provide staff training and instructions on correct handling, storing and disposable of hazardous substances. Some of the products included under this act are:

✧ Chemical cleaners
✧ Surgical spirit
✧ Witch hazel
✧ Chemical sterilising solutions
✧ Bleaches.

The Work Place (Health, Safety, Welfare) Regulations 1992

These regulations set the provision of safe premises in which to work and the minimum standard of facilities to be found within a clinic/salon.

The Personal Protective Equipment At Work Act 1992

This Act states that the employer is obliged to provide free all suitable personal equipment, for example disposable gloves, face masks and uniforms to all employees who may be exposed to a risk in the work place. Under this Act employees are obliged to report damage or loss of this equipment to the employer and must not misuse it.

The Manual Handling Operations Regulations 1992

Under this Act all employers must carry out an assessment of each employee's capability to carry or move stock. Also to provide training on safe working practice, for example to prevent injury when lifting, carrying or unpacking stock etc.

Reporting Of Injuries, Disease And Dangerous Occurrences Regulations 1985 (RIDDOR)

Under these Regulations all accidents that occur in the clinic/salon, must be recorded in an accident book, with details of the incident to include the following:
✧ Name, age of injured person.
✧ Date and time of accident.
✧ Brief description of accident and nature of injury, for example burning to left hand, fainted and hit back of the head, etc.
✧ Place where accident occurred, for example cubicle 1.
✧ Action taken, for example recovery position and if an ambulance was required.

Under this regulation the Health and Safety Executive requires immediate notification if anyone dies or is seriously injured in connection with a work place accident, or if anyone is off work longer than 3 days, as a result of sustaining a work place injury, or if they have a specific industrial disease or disorder or a potentially infectious condition which is confirmed by a doctor or hospital, for example Hepatitis, Menigitis.

The employer is then obliged to send a report to the local authority environmental health department within 7 days, although in some cases the general medical practitioner will notify the department.

The Electricity At Work Regulations 1989

These Regulations are concerned with the employer ensuring that all electrical equipment used within the clinic/salon is installed safely and in good working order, with regular maintenance checks and servicing by an appropriately qualified electrician. All maintenance checks and repairs etc must be recorded within a log book, with date and signature of electrician. This log book may be required in the event of a serious incident or prosecution. Equipment must display a pass or fail P.A.T. inspection label.

The Local Government (Miscellaneous Provisions) Act 1982

This Act enables the local council authority to set their own bye-laws, and regulations regarding clinics/salons who provide electrolysis treatments. All electrologists or therapists are obliged to register their premises in order to carry out electrolysis treatments, and may be inspected by a local authority environmental health officer periodically, and in the event of any breaches of legislation, the environmental health officer has the power to impose a hefty financial fine and even enforce closure of premises. Registration of premises involves the electrologist having to pay an annual fee which, like the standards, varies greatly with each local authority, from county to county. The standards involve the following:

✧ Cleanliness of the premises and fittings, walls and floor surfaces etc

✧ Personal hygiene of staff working within premises

✧ Methods of cleaning and sterilising equipment etc

✧ Hygienic storage and disposal of waste products, for example double sealed waste bags, and all waste bins must be emptied as often as necessary and with a minimum of once a day

✧ The correct disposal of contaminated waste, for example used needles into a sharps box, which when full is collected for incineration usually by a local authority agency

✧ A constant supply of hot and cold water, with sufficient sinks for employees working within premises

✧ Adequate toilet facilities for staff and general public

✧ First aid box

✧ Sufficient storage space, to reduce risk of cross infection

✧ No smoking or eating within clinic/salon treatment areas

✧ Where possible use disposable products to reduce risk of cross infection, for example disposable couch paper, disposal tissue, needles, gloves etc

✧ Good ventilation and lighting with adequate heating to provide a comfortable working temperature between 20–25°C.

All electrologists wishing to open their own premises should contact the local authority's environmental health department to find out local standards, prior to application for registration being made.

The Code of Practice of Hygiene in Beauty Salons and Allied Clinics

This applies general terms of the Health and Safety at Work Act to the industry. Basically this code sets down guidelines similar to those imposed by the local authority bye-laws.

Fire Precaution Act 1971

This Act deals with fire prevention and emergency escape routes etc. All clinic/salon employers with 20 or more employees must apply for a fire certificate, have the premises inspected regularly and follow strict regulations governing fire precautions.

Employers must ensure the following occur:
✧ That all fire escape routes and exit doors are clearly signposted and kept free from obstruction at all time.
✧ Smoke alarms must be fitted.
✧ Fire doors must be fitted to limit the spread of fire in the event of it occurring, where required.
✧ A range of fire fighting equipment is available and in good working order to deal with the types of fire which may arise.
✧ All employees undertake regular fire evacuation training/practice and are familiar with how to use firefighting equipment.

First Aid Regulations 1981

Under these Regulations, employers are required to provide adequate and appropriate equipment and facilities for first aid depending on the number of staff employed. Both self employed therapists and employers must provide a First Aid Kit containing standard contents. The box must have a green area with a white cross on it.

Consumer Protection Act 1987

Under this Act the general public are protected when purchasing either goods or services. Any products must be safe for use on clients during treatments, or safe to be sold as retail products, for example after care lotions. The act also includes preventing misleading the public over price information etc regarding goods and services.

The Sale and Supply of Goods Act 1994

This Act covers implied terms of the the contract of sale between the retailer and the customer, and states:
✧ that the standard of goods provided must be of reasonable merchantable quality, described accurately and fit the purpose for which they are intended
✧ any services provided must be carried out with skill and care within an acceptable time constraint for a reasonable fee.

Insurance

All practising electrologists, whether employers, employees or self employed must be covered by insurance, The type of policy required will vary with each individual according to the type of business and services offered.

The Employer's Liability Regulations 1998

If you are an employer you are legally bound under the this act to have employer's liability (compulsory) insurance. This certificate of insurance must be displayed within the work place. Employer's liability insurance covers the employer against claims made by staff for injury or illness sustained during the course of their work.

Other insurances which need to be considered are:

Public Liability Insurance

> This type of insurance covers the clinic/salon with regard to the general public being accidentally injured, or their property damaged during their visit to the clinic/salon etc. It is advisable to take out this type of policy.

Vicarious Liability

> An employer is responsible legally for the actions or negligence of his employees. This means that both may be sued for compensation or damages in the event of action being taken by a client.

Treatment Risk

> This type of insurance covers the electrologist against the client suing with regard to accidental damage or injury which may occur as a result of treatment, for example permanent skin damage etc.

Advanced Treatments

> An additional cover is required to carry out treatments such as red vein/capillaries, and skin tags and is usually added to treatment risk policy.

Building Insurance

> This type of policy covers the premises for storm damage, fire, flooding, and burglary etc.

Contents Insurance

> This type of policy covers the contents of the building usually for accidental damage to stock, equipment, all fixtures and fittings etc.

Consequential loss

> This type of policy covers loss of annual profits as a result of a natural disaster, for example storm damage, fire etc and business having to suspend trading whilst repairs are carried out.

Health Insurances

Permanent health insurance is worth considering if you are either self employed or the main breadwinner. In the event of either short, long term illness or disability you are guaranteed a regular income which should reflect your earning power, depending on the type of premium paid.

There are many types of policies available which can be tailored to suit your individual requirements as follows:

General personal accident insurance, which covers you for specific benefits such as, loss of limbs, eyesight or life. Critical illness insurance which insures you, should cancer, heart conditions and permanent disability etc permanently prevent you from returning to your occupation.

Insurance can therefore be taken out to insure one or more areas of the body, for example some models insure their legs for vast sums of money against loss, damage, etc. An electrologist therefore may wish to insure her hands, arms and eyesight specifically against illness or accidental damage.

It is recommended that you seek independent advice on insurance in order to get your policy tailored to meet your specific requirements.

Whatever types of insurance you decide upon remember to read the small print carefully to ensure you are getting the policy requirements you specifically need. If you belong to a professional body they often arrange membership insurance at a reduced fee.

review**questions**

Q1 Name two methods used to sterilise pre-packed sterilised needles.

Q2 State the most effective method of sterilisation suitable for forceps/tweezers.

Q3 Name the micro-organism which reproduces by binary fusion.

Q4 List four types of viruses.

Q5 Name the type of bacteria responsible for the skin condition impetigo.

Q6 List three conditions necessary for the growth of bacteria.

Q7 State two reasons for pre-cleaning tools prior to sterilisation.

Q8 Name the Act which requires all clinics etc wishing to provide electrolysis services to register with the local council authority.

Q9 List four types of health insurance available.

Q10 Name the insurance which is compulsory for all employers to have.

Q11 Define the term risk assessment.

Q12 State which Act sets down the responsibilities of the employer and employee.

The consultation | 7

This chapter aims to give an insight into the procedures and psychological factors involved in carrying out a professional consultation.

Psychological factors to be considered

It takes a great deal of personal courage for any individual suffering from unwanted facial or body hairgrowth, to actually walk through the salon door and discuss the problem with a complete stranger.

Remember, many people may have already sought medical advice from an unsympathetic GP who gave them no solution, and have spent years suffering the embarrassment of unwanted hairgrowth. Those more fortunate may have reached your door sooner as a result of having a more progressive and sympathetic GP or an informed friend.

A percentage of all female clients seeking treatment will feel they are unusually 'freakish or unfeminine' to have this unsightly problem and will genuinely believe they are alone in the world with their excess hairgrowth. Other clients do not even tell their partners or family about their unwanted hairgrowth, choosing to keep it hidden as a dark, shameful secret to be dealt with quietly and alone in the bathroom, during the early or late hours of the day. They may trust only you or their GP with this secret, perhaps telling their loved ones, they are having oestopathy or chiropody etc. Thus, the relationship between the client and electrologist is one of confidentiality and trust.

Many clients will be shy and introverted, tearful with a loss of self confidence and low self-esteem – possibly suffering bouts of depression. Some will talk with their hand over their mouth to hide the problem. I have even had those clients who preferred to wear a sticky plaster over the hairgrowth. Others may be aggressive, argumentative and defensive to hide their feelings of embarrassment. Whatever personality characteristics the client may exhibit at the start of a course of treatment, their personality will be changed by the experience of electrolysis. As the treatment progresses and the hairgrowth disappears, the client's self confidence will grow. A shy introverted client can blossom before your eyes, becoming more radiant, outgoing and start to live life to the full. While the aggressive defensive client will become more mellow, friendly and happy generally.

Women often confide, after successful treatment, that at the start they felt ugly, unfeminine and depressed with no interest in anything and that now they can't really explain just how much electrolysis has changed their life for the better. To the electrologist these comments make you realise just how privileged you are, to have a career you enjoy and at the same time one that enables you to help people and enjoy their newly found happiness.

The consultation

A consultation is an appointment which is usually free of charge for a potential client, to view the premises, meet the electrologist and find out about the treatment. The electrologist should ensure that both his/her personal appearance and the salon are immaculate and ready for inspection.

The electrologist needs to use both verbal and non-verbal techniques during the consultation. He/she should have a calming, sympathetic approach towards the client. This will soothe the client's worries and help with their self-esteem, regarding their individual hairgrowth problem. This in turn helps the client to relax and speak more freely about the hair problem. It also enables the electrologist and client to build up a rapport.

When the client arrives, greet them by name and introduce yourself in a confident, professional and friendly manner. These first few minutes are crucial and almost certainly decide whether you gain a new client or not. Show your potential client to a quiet, private area, position yourself on a level with the client and ensure that your body language is open. Maintain eye contact and smile. This will certainly help the client to relax. Every consultation will be different regardless of gender, but the following should always be considered: observe the client's body language. Consider whether she or he is nervous, fidgety, has arms crossed and if she/he makes eye contact. This information will enable you to gauge the client's emotional state.

Explain clearly that you will have to record a few personal details, regarding her or his medical history, contra-indications, lifestyle etc, to establish whether or not the client is suitable for treatment. Explain that electrolysis is not appropriate for everyone and do not be frightened to say if the client's lifestyle prevents her or him from being a good candidate for electrolysis. You can offer her/him alternative short-term treatments.

This is also the time to find out what the client's expectations are. What does she/he already know about electrolysis? Let the client know they can interrupt you at any time to ask questions or clarify information.

You will also need to explain that electrolysis is a course of treatment and not a miracle cure. It is a long-term solution to unwanted hairgrowth. It works by gradually thinning the hair problem out, just like watching a man going bald. Firstly there are 200 hairs, then 150, 100, 50, 20 until eventually there is no hair growth left. Success!! Be honest and explain that there will be a percentage of regrowth, and why. State that it is difficult to predict how long a course of treatment will take, as everyone responds differently and it requires personal and financial commitment and time from both the client and electrolysist for treatment to be successful.

Confirm that the client understands this and assure her or him of your ability, qualifications, hygiene practices and commitment to solve this problem.

Ask the client what the hairgrowth problem is, even if it is an obvious one. Never assume that a female client with top lip hairgrowth wants that area treated, she may well be seeking treatment for another area, and this would only lead to the client being embarrassed and offended.

Discuss how long the problem has existed, trying to establish the probable cause, for example puberty, pregnancy, etc and any previous methods of hair removal and frequency of their use. You will need to ask the client if you can carry out a physical examination of the area, to establish the skin and hair type. This will enable you to tailor the treatment to meet the client's individual needs. Discussion should follow on the skin and hair type present and the best probable method of epilation to use, ie shortwave diathermy, galvanic or the blend method.

I would suggest you then offer a short test treatment to establish the client's pain threshold, strength and depth of hairgrowth, prior to discussing the cost of treatment, frequency of treatment and duraton of each session for this particular client.

Finally, explain what the skin tissues will look like, and that there are no side effects, when being treated by a competent and skilled professional. Although there will be an initial localised reaction by the skin tissues, such as localised swelling, erythema and warmth, but this will disappear quickly, depending on skin type and sensitivity – usually within a few hours. Check if the client has any more questions for you to answer and confirm that she/he fully understands the procedure, time and cost involved before embarking on a course of treatment. If the client is confident that this is what she or he wants, you can complete the record card and ask her or him to sign it if the details are correct. You now have two choices, either to offer the client a short immediate treatment, if time permits, or book a treatment for a later date. Your potential client now should feel comfortable with the salon environment, the electrologist and the idea of solving a long-term problem.

Contra-indications

A contra-indication is a condition which prevents or restricts the electrologist from carrying out the treatment. However, there are many contra-indications which are treatable if medical advice is sought and received:

Heart disorders
Rarely cause problems with treatment, but should always be referred for medical approval due to the variety of heart conditions.

Pace-makers
Require medical permission as the high frequency current may affect the rhythm of a unit, in which case no treatment can be given. The newer models are better insulated and can allow treatment to occur depending on type and GP approval.

Epilepsy

Treatable if the condition has been controlled by medication and the GP gives permission. The electrical impulses to the brain may be disturbed and trigger a fit.

Diabetes

Diabetic skins have a slower healing rate and are prone to skin eruptions and infection and therefore should be treated with extra care after medical approval is given.

Hepatitis B

This is highly contagious and, like the HIV virus, can be transmitted via body fluids and blood. The electrolysist should seek medical advice as to whether or not treatment should go ahead.

Generally the decision is left to the electrolysist to decide if they feel they can deal with the extra hygiene precautions necessary, which are essential if treating these conditions, to ensure no cross-infection occurs.

It is recommended that all electrologist's are vaccinated against Hepatitis B for their own protection.

Steroid drugs

Often encourage hairgrowth, regardless of whether appliction is internal or external.

Endocrine disorders

May result in increased hairgrowth in the male pattern and medical advice is required to help reduce hairgrowth.

Metal plates and pins

If present in treatment area they may heat up due to the electrical current or chemical action with galvanic current, which will cause burning of tissues.

Cardiovascular disorders

Need to be referred to GP, as anti-coagulant drugs can affect success of treatment and healing process, which depends on the success of coagulation and cauterisation of the dermal papilla area of the follicle.

Loss of tactile sensation, for example Bells palsy, strokes, de-nervated areas

It is important that the client can respond to hot and cold sensation in the treatment area, to prevent skin damage resulting from incorrect use of current.

Skin disorders and diseases

Any condition which may be contagious or infectious prohibits a treatment, for example bacterial, viral and fungal infections.

(See Chapter 4 Dermatology).

Hairy moles

Can be treated by the experienced electrologist with medical permission. Due to the nature of moles, they need a biopsy to be checked for signs of malignancy as heat could stimulate growth of cancerous cells.

Pregnancy

Abdomen or breast areas should not be treated during pregnancy as areas are tender at this time. Hairgrowth often forms temporarily during pregnancy and disappears after childbirth and, therefore, may not require treatment.

Drugs

Certain medications can adversely affect electrolysis treatment, particularly steroid drugs. It is, therefore, necessary for the electrologist to establish the nature of the drugs and their affect on the hairgrowth, skin type etc.

Cuts/abrasions/bruising

These areas should be avoided due to the risk of cross infection and sensitivity of tissues.

Emotional problems

If your client is having severe emotional problems this will affect the treatment programme, because the client's pain threshold may be low given that the client is unable to relax. As such, treatment time may have to be shorter. More time will have to be allocated for reassuring and comforting the client with regard to treatment procedures and success.

Young people

Require parental permission due to legal implications for any one under 16 years of age, also hormonal imbalances can correct themselves during this period.

Asthma

Anxiety over treatment or stress can trigger an asthmatic attack, which results in the narrowing of the airways, creating difficulty in breathing. This condition requires written medical consent from the GP. If treatment has been agreed by the GP, particular attention should be given to the positioning of the client.

Dermagraphic skin condition

This is a congenital sensitivity to any form of skin friction, and results in swelling of the tissues shortly after treatment. There are no long-term adverse effects, and treatment may continue if the client wishes, as the condition usually lasts less than 24 hours.

Areas contra-indicated to electrolysis

Nostrils and ears. Nostril area is very moist and there is a risk of infection due to the nature of the area. The ears are sensitive and very vascular.

The pain threshold factor

As an electrologist you will treat a variety of clients. A factor that you will need to consider is their pain threshold, as each individual's pain threshold will vary considerably.

Pain is felt by the sensory nerve endings in the dermis tissue.

What is the pain threshold? Quite simply it is synapse fatigue. A synapse is the point of contact between two nerve cells (neurons), which transmit messages to and from the brain. Repeated messages tire the synapses causing them to send the messages more slowly. This is synapse fatigue. The threshold is the level at which the electrologist works for client comfort.

An electrologist must consider this when formulating a treatment plan. It is better to always work across a small area, with probes slightly closer together than normal. The nerve endings in that area then continuously receive the same message, so that the sensation of the treatment registers less with the nervous system, creating a numbing effect which is called electro-anaesthetism. However care must be taken to monitor the skin surface reaction. For the clients comfort it is better not to jump from one area to another.

There are several other things the electrologist can do to influence the clients pain threshold level. They include:

✧ the use of calming verbal techniques to instil confidence throughout the treatment. This will distract the client, taking her mind off the treatment and allowing her/him to relax more

✧ Also cooling of the skin after hair removal refreshes the tissues and distracts the nerve endings.

The higher the client's pain threshold, the more the client can tolerate. Therefore, the aim of the treatment is to work as closely as possible to the pain threshold, thus using the maximum amount of intensity the client can comfortably take, without causing undue discomfort or trauma to the skin tissues.

The professional appearance and manner of the electrologist will also instil confidence in the client and, therefore, have an affect on her or his pain threshold.

Factors which influence the pain threshold:

✧ client's emotional state
✧ confidence in the electrologist
✧ general health of the client
✧ time of the month, if premenstrual
✧ area to be treated
✧ the electrologist's ability and degree of professionalism
✧ strength of current and type of machine
✧ explanation of treatment
✧ duration of treatment time
✧ spacing of probes
✧ verbal reassurance from the electrologist
✧ water retention can affect treatment due to tissue fluid pressing down on sensory nerve corpuscles and follicle openings being tighter
✧ pain threshold is also lower just before a meal due to a drop in blood sugar level. Timing of appointments should be carefully planned particularly when treating diabetic clients.

The record card

Should be started at the initial consultation and completed after each client's treatment. It is a record for you, the electrologist, and any other member of staff who treats a client for the first time and also a record for your insurance company.

It should, therefore, be a full and accurate account of the hair problem and record:
✧ its probable cause
✧ previous methods of hair removal and their effects on skin and hair
✧ relevant GP referral notes
✧ skin conditions, discolouration, scarring present prior to treatment
✧ specific reference points for future treatment adaptations with regard to:
     ✧ spacing out of probes
     ✧ adaptation of current intensity
     ✧ healing responses of skin tissues.

The client should, after the initial consultation, be asked to check the information you have recorded and sign the record card to state that the information she has given you is true.

There are numerous record cards available, some are very detailed others have minimal requirements, so care should be taken when purchasing them.

See sample record card for information required on a record card.

Electrolysis Record Card	
Client's Name:..	Doctor's Name:..
Address:	Address: ....
....	....
................................Tel No:..................................	................................Tel No:..................................
Date of Birth:	

Medical History...	GP Referral: Yes/No
Drugs	Contraceptive Pill/HRT/Diuretics/Steroids/Anti-depressants
Contra-indications	Hepatitis B/HIV/Heart disorders/Pacemakers/Diabetes/Epilepsy/High or Low blood pressure/Thrombosis/Embolism/Skin disorder/Skin disease/Loss of tactile sensation/Deficiency of hot or cold response/Cuts and abrasions/Metal plates and pins/Herpes simplex and abdomen in pregnancy/Severe bruising
Hair Type	Single/Compound/Curly/Straight/Fine/Coarse
Skin Type	Dry/Sensitive/Oily/Combination/Dehydrated problem
Healing Rate	Good/Poor/Average
Nervous/Non-nervous client	
Previous Hairgrowth Treatment	Plucking/Waxing/Shaving/Cutting/Delipatory Creams/Electrolysis
Probable Cause of Hairgrowth	Puberty/Pregnancy/Pre-Post Menopause/Medication/Hereditary/Surgical/Topical Stimulation/Emotional/Endocrine Disorder
Areas to be Treated	Top Lip/Chin/Neck/Eyebrows/Legs/Arms/Bikini Line/Abdomen/Breasts
Homecare Advice	....
Retail Products	....
Additional Notes	....
Client's Signature	....

Date	Area Treated	Current Intensity	Method	Treatment Time	Needle Size	Skin Reaction	Therapist	Cost

review questions

Q1 List four benefits of a consultation for the electrologist.

Q2 State four things which should be recorded on a record card following electrolysis treatment.

Q3 List six qualities required in an electrologist.

Q4 State why it is necessary to discuss previous methods of hair removal and frequency.

Q5 Name four medical conditions which require GP referral prior to treatment.

Q6 List four ways in which a client may benefit from a consultation before electrolysis treatment.

Q7 Name four factors which may affect the clients pain threshold.

Q8 State why the client's body language needs to be observed during the consultation by the electrologist.

Q9 Name two areas of the body contra-indicated to electrolysis.

Q10 State why it is important that the client understands that electrolysis is not a one-off treatment.

Q11 List six pieces of information to be considered when devising a treatment plan for a client.

Q12 State two reasons for keeping accurate and up to date record cards.

Probing techniques and current adaptations | 8

The aim of this chapter is to introduce good practical skills and to show you how to modify treatments to suit the individual needs of each client.

How to probe

Trainee electrolysists should initially learn to probe on oranges, where the peel has large pores similar to the skin. An electrologist must be comfortable with handling the needle holder and forceps prior to skin probing to prevent errors in technique.

Successful electrolysis depends on several factors. Good probing technique and placing the needle in the matrix papilla area are essential, as is adjustment of current intensity and its application time.

The trainee electrolysist should select a prepacked sterile needle size 004 or 005 (depending on make), when starting probing for the first time (as the larger needle diameters are usually less flexible, enabling better control than the finer size 003 needle) and insert it into the needle holder using sterile forceps, following manufacturer's instructions and observing all hygiene precautions.

The needle holder is always held between the thumb and index finger. It should be held firmly, but gently, and feel comfortable. It is easier if the trainee rests her third finger against the orange or client's skin whilst probing, as this holds her hand steady allowing her to probe with more ease.

The forceps should be held between the thumb and index finger of the left hand, whilst the needle holder is held between the index and middle fingers of the right hand. This is for ease of changeover sequence and the index and middle finger of the left hand help to stretch the skin being treated aiding insertion by opening the follicle mouth and reducing client discomfort. Reverse all above if a left-handed operator.

The needle size should mirror the size of the hair diameter being treated. The aim is to insert the needle probing smoothly in the direction of the hairgrowth, at the angle at which the hair emerges from the follicle mouth, entering under and parallel to the hair, sliding smoothly into the follicle alongside the hair root in the matrix area.

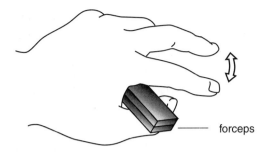

forceps

1. Stretch skin tissues with middle and index finger for ease of insertion.

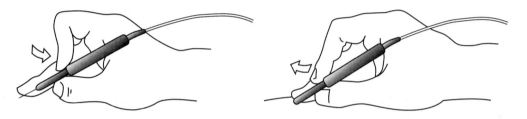

2. Follow insertion guidelines and withdraw needle at same angle at which it was inserted

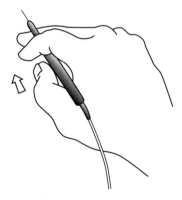

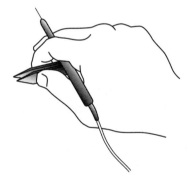

3. The body of the needle holder should now be positioned between second and third fingers.

4. Index and thumb fingers hold forceps and position them at opening of follicle and grasp hair and remove it in the direction of growth smoothly without traction. Placing it on a tissue or cotton wool pad ready for inspection of hair growth stage.

Hand positioning

When probing has become more accurate and the technique is smooth and controlled with no obvious shaking, the current can be introduced to the matrix papilla area and discharged. Only remove the needle probe when the current has stopped flowing. Very gently stretch the skin, focusing on the treated hair, bringing the forceps over from the left hand to the working right hand (reverse if left-handed) and remove the hair, by taking forceps to follicle opening and removing the hair in the direction of growth. If the hair has been treated with the correct amount of current intensity and application time, it should slide freely from the follicle, and be placed on a tissue. Its root structure can then be observed to help the electrologist decide on the stage of hairgrowth and the depth of probing needed, by looking at the distance from the hair bulb to the point of the hair. This indicates the follicle depth, and allows the electrologist to gauge how far to insert the needle into the follicle.

The aim of the electrologist is, therefore, to achieve a smooth and steady insertion, following the direction of hairgrowth. It should be neither too fast or too slow. This enables the electrologist to develop a sense of touch, which is essential when probing the follicle as there is a natural resistance present – the base of the follicle. If you push past this you inflict pain on the client and damage to the basal cell layer resulting in blood spots or scarring. This sense of touch comes with experience and will become instinctive, guiding you to the base of the follicle and allowing you to make judgements on hair type and depth.

There should be continuity of treatment, no stabbing or hesitation when selecting hairgrowth. Treatment should be continuous with darkest thickest longest, most visible hairs treated first, or the hairs causing the client the most distress, then in later sessions treat the finer or missed hairgrowth.

Points to remember
✧ Always check the equipment before use
✧ Sterilise tweezers
✧ Always use a cold light magnifying lamp
✧ Always use the same needle diameter as the hair
✧ Always insert in direction of hairgrowth and under the hair for a smooth insertion
✧ Always insert at the same angle as the hair emerges from the follicle mouth
✧ Always treat the dark coarse, most visible hairgrowth first
✧ Always scatter your work in one area working on one in four hairs to prevent heat convergence
✧ Never enter or leave the follicle whilst the current is flowing
✧ Always check epilated hairgrowth root for probing guidance
✧ If hairs are curly ignore the tail end, look at the hair emerging from the follicle mouth only
✧ If hairs are long, trim them down with scissors to make probing easier
✧ Always work with a relaxed hand and insert slowly to begin with to develop your sense of touch.

The effects of incorrect probing techniques

It is essential that as an electrologist you can recognise and avoid common probing faults. Faults in probing technique will prevent you from reaching a high standard of expertise.

When probing there should be no skin dimpling or depression, if your probing is accurate. If there is, slowly pull your needle back until the skin's surface evens out.

After treatment there should be no visible signs that treatment has taken place, except for localised erythema-redness and swelling.

Probing too shallow

As most of the current heat is concentrated at the tip of the needle when the insertion into the skin tissue is too shallow, the heat will disperse into the top layers of the epidermis and may severely burn it. The skin will blister up around the needle in a white raised ring and stick to the needle (in some cases) forming an erythema (red background). This will leave a superficial scar causing a red brown scab to form. The effect on the hairgrowth is minimal as no heat is likely to reach the matrix papilla area.

Probing too deep

This occurs when the needle is pushed through the base of the follicle into the dermis skin. This causes severe burning to both the basal layer of the epidermis and the dermis, which in turn inhibits growth of new cells. Any new cells growing are permanently damaged and this results in permanent pitted scarring on the surface of the skin. Blood spotting – micro heamorrhaging – will occur and the client suffers pain.

Needle point movement

This can lead to the current being released into the surrounding tissues and, therefore, reducing the effect at the hair root of the cauterisation. The skin tissues become damaged as the current escapes into the surrounding tissues resulting in either surface burns, depending on depth of probe, or scarring and client discomfort.

Probing into the follicle wall

This occurs when the shallow needle probe passes through the follicle wall, causing surface burns, possible scarring to the basal cell layer lining the hair follicle and damage to the capillaries in the area. There is no affect on hairgrowth as the current is not placed near the matrix papilla area.

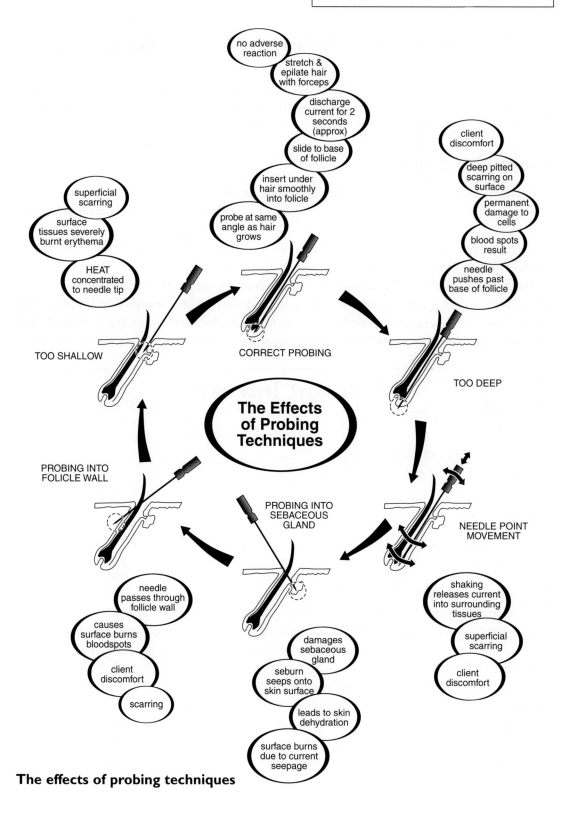

no adverse reaction

stretch & epilate hair with forceps

discharge current for 2 seconds (approx)

slide to base of follicle

insert under hair smoothly into folicle

probe at same angle as hair grows

client discomfort

deep pitted scarring on surface

permanent damage to cells

blood spots result

needle pushes past base of follicle

superficial scarring

surface tissues severely burnt erythema

HEAT concentrated to needle tip

TOO SHALLOW

CORRECT PROBING

TOO DEEP

The Effects of Probing Techniques

PROBING INTO FOLICLE WALL

PROBING INTO SEBACEOUS GLAND

NEEDLE POINT MOVEMENT

needle passes through follicle wall

causes surface burns bloodspots

client discomfort

scarring

damages sebaceous gland

seburn seeps onto skin surface

leads to skin dehydration

surface burns due to current seepage

shaking releases current into surrounding tissues

superficial scarring

client discomfort

The effects of probing techniques

Probing into the sebaceous gland

Occurs when the needle pierces the sebaceous gland due to inaccurate probing. The current cauterises cells in the area which leads to the drying out of skin tissues in the area and sebum seepage onto the skin surface. There is a risk of the current seeping up on to the surface and causing surface burns.

Habits to avoid

Stroking the hair or skin and any undue hesitation between insertions, leads to an inefficient treatment. Loss of rhythm and continuity may result in loss of client confidence in the electrologist.

The hair should not be lifted or rotated around the needle before insertion. This can lead to incorrect angle of insertion and poor treatment results.

Never do a double depression on the current switch, which gives two bursts of current to the follicle during a single insertion. The second depression can easily move the needle, which may then pierce the base of the follicle or move the needle onto the wall of the follicle. This can lead to incorrect current distribution and scarring, due to a build up of current.

Current Intensity

Factors which influence the current intensity level selected by the electrologist include:
- ✧ the client's pain threshold
- ✧ the skin type and its sensitivity
- ✧ the hair type and its texture
- ✧ the area to be treated
- ✧ the needle size
- ✧ previous treatments given.

The success of electrolysis treatment, regardless of method used, depends on the accuracy of your probing technique, your intensity and its application time. You should aim to deliver the maximum amount of current intensity with an appropriate application time, to the matrix papilla area to bring about maximum tissue destruction, allowing the hair to slide freely and smoothly out of the hair follicle, without causing undue discomfort to the client, or any adverse affects to the surrounding skin tissues.

Always start with a low current intensity and gradually increase it till your client feels the sensation, continue to increase the current within your client's pain threshold and skin tolerance, until the hair slides freely, without any traction from the follicle. This current intensity and application time used is the best working point for the hairgrowth in the immediate area. This will vary all over the treatment area due to the variety of hairs within the area.

Deep, coarse, terminal hairs will require a higher current intensity than fine vellus or shallow terminal hair. If a hair is resistant then you can turn up the current intensity and treat once more, usually with successful results if needle placement is accurate. If, however, you have a client with strong hairgrowth but she cannot tolerate the high current intensity required you have another option to reduce the current intensity and increase your application time, normally this method will achieve successful hair removal without causing client discomfort, providing probing is accurate.

Remember, if you increase the current intensity, you will require less current application time (high and fast method) and if you increase your application time you will therefore require less current intensity (this is the low and slow method). If your hair fails to epilate after the second attempt, it is advisable to pluck it out, to prevent an infection resulting. The body may treat it as a foreign body.

Incorrect adjustment of current intensity will cause a number of problems including:
✧ a higher percentage of regrowth hairs, due to too little high frequency current and under treatment of matrix papilla area
✧ too much high frequency current can result in overtreatment of skin tissues, causing erythema, excessive swelling, blanching of tissues and surface burns
✧ too much galvanic current will result in weeping follicles.

Heating patterns

During electrolysis a fine needle probe enters the hair follicle and travels to the lower region of the epidermis, where there is a concentration of water and moisture within the tissues. Once placement of the needle has occurred a high frequency current is released into this moist tissue, which readily responds to it. As the needle diameter is small, the current is attracted to the tip of the needle where it is concentrated, creating a pattern which generates heat. Ideally the heating pattern should be teardrop or peardrop in shape. Having commenced at the tip of the needle the heat slowly moves up and out evenly towards the skin surface, without ever reaching it. This allows for the matrix papilla area of the follicle to be treated without the surface tissues being adversely affected. The size and shape of the heating pattern can be influenced by a number of factors.

Moisture Gradient
The moisture content varies through the epidermis with the most moisture being in the lower layers. When treating deep coarse hair growth with a moist skin the following should be considered:

The moisture content will vary very little from the top to the bottom of the hair follicle, therefore extra care is required to ensure that the heating pattern produced by the high frequency current does not reach the surface tissues before sufficient destruction had occurred at the matrix. If it does, the result would be burning and blistering of surface skin tissues.

Effects of increasing current application time on heating patterns

When you increase your current application time you will find that the heating pattern you are creating within the skin tissues will change, expanding in both width and height thus covering a greater surface area. Care must be taken to ensure that the heating pattern never travels to the skin's surface, otherwise surface damage may result in the form of scarring, blistering etc. The electrologist must therefore balance the length of time the current is applied for against the level of current intensity.

The effects of current intensity on the heating patterns

The current intensity needs to be high enough to ensure that the high frequency current travels to the tip of the needle, where it starts to develop evenly, up and out, to bring about coagulation of the skin tissues. If the current intensity is too low coagulation will not occur and the heating pattern will not start at the needle tip but commence further up the needle shaft, reaching the surface tissues quickly and not achieving tissue coagulation of the lower follicle. Coagulation only occurs when tissues reach a temperature of between 43–54°C, with an average being 52°C.

The diameter of the needle and its effects on heating patterns

A tapered needle increases the heating effect at the tip of the needle, and is ideal for short-wave diathermy. The needle diameter affects the current intensity and size of the heating pattern produced and the sensation felt by the client. For example, if you treat a client with a current intensity of 25 milliamps, with a 003 needle size, this smaller needle diameter will produce a more intense, strongly concentrated heating pattern which is highly effective in producing tissue destruction, but may result in client discomfort or pain due to the stronger sensation felt. However, if you take the same 25 milliamp intensity and pass it through a larger needle diameter, it will produce a less intense heating pattern as the current has been spread over a wider area of skin, diluting or weakening the intensity of heat and its effectiveness in tissue destruction, but producing a milder sensation in the client.

Remember the needle diameter should always match the size of the hair diameter, and you will probably need to change needle size at some stage of treatment. As hairgrowth becomes finer a smaller needle diameter will be required, due to the reduction in hair diameter, for example if treatment commenced with a size 004 needle it may change to a size 003 at some stage.

Needle depth and its effect on the heating pattern

The depth of the needle insertion will have an effect on the sensation experienced by the client, in that the shallower the needle lies in the skin tissues, the thinner the area it has to distribute the current, and the more intense and hot the sensation felt, resulting in blistering and surface burns.

If the needle probe is correctly placed, there should be no adverse effects on the surface tissues and coagulation of the lower follicle should occur.

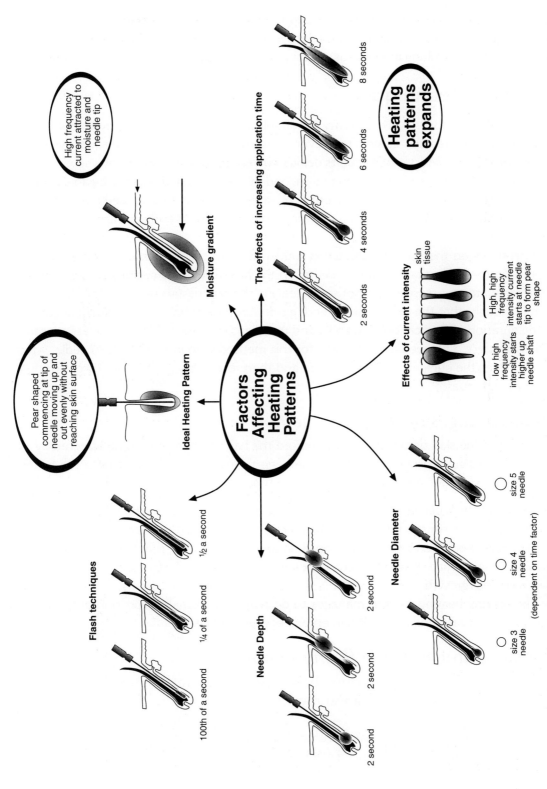

Factors affecting heating patterns

However if the needle depth is too deep the base of the follicle wall will be punctured and the basal layer of the epidermis and dermis tissue will be badly affected by the high frequency current, resulting in tissue destruction, and pitted scarring to surface tissues.

The flash technique

This method of shortwave diathermy is suitable for fine straight hairgrowth and clients with a low pain threshold. It aims to deliver a very high intensity of high frequency current for a reduced time. Most modern units deliver current for one hundredth of a second, older units between a fraction of a second to a second. It is a controlled delivery by an automatic timer. When the high frequency current is released, it travels to the needle tip quickly to form a very intense narrow heating pattern, which rapidly extends towards the skin surface.

The effect on the skin tissues of this sudden flash of high, intense current is to bring about electro-dessication, which occurs when the high frequency current comes into contact with water moisture and vaporises it, leaving the skin tissues dry and dehydrated.

It is thought that the client's nerve endings do not have time to respond to the current, as the duration of application is so short and the client therefore experiences less sensation and discomfort. The needle most suited for this method is an insulated steel needle, which concentrates the current to the needle tip and therefore helps to prevent current rising to the surface tissues.

Disadvantages of the flash method

Blanching of the skin tissues may occur before the hair has had time to be affected by the current successfully, especially with coarse deep terminal hairgrowth, due to the heating pattern being narrow and reaching the surface tissues.

An extremely high percentage of regrowth with this method due to the following:
✧ The needle shares the follicle with the hair, which may push the needle off centre
✧ With the shorter current application time and the narrower the heating pattern, heat takes time to build up and become concentrated, thus less destruction occurs, resulting in more hairgrowth
✧ The narrow heating pattern manages to destroy only a small proportion of the matrix papilla area, resulting in a high percentage of regrowth hair.

The advantages of the flash method

Suitable for sensitive skins as its narrow heating pattern concentrates the current to the tip of the needle, when combined with an insulated needle and one hundreth of a second current application time.

For clients who have a low pain threshold and fine hairgrowth this method can be very successful, if used by an experienced electrologist.

Regrowth

Every client requires a different treatment. Some will need weekly treatments initially, for an extensive hairgrowth problem, whilst others may require monthly treatment for a short period of time.

Regardless of the type and extent of the problem being treated, there is always a percentage of regrowth with electrolysis, and the client should be made aware of this fact. If the client does not understand that there will be regrowth for a number of reasons, he/she will become despondent and give up treatment as her expectations will be unrealistic. It is vital that you explain how electrolysis works, that it is a thinning out process and not an instant miracle cure.

Even with an experienced electrologist there will be a percentage of regrowth. This may be anything between 25 per cent to 50 per cent of the original hairgrowth treated, regardless of hair type due to a number of reasons.

The best time to epilate a hair is generally in the early anagen stage, as the follicle is shallow and straight, making probing easier. Theoretically, if probing and current are accurate you may achieve successful destruction of the follicle, resulting in no regrowth. However, in reality this does not occur every time.

You can recognise regrowth hairs as they are smaller in diameter, lighter in colour and softer in texture. The hairs are well spaced out in the area previously treated, and these hairs grow from a shallower follicle now.

There are a number of reasons why regrowth occurs. They include:

◇ **True regrowth** is hairgrowth that you have previously treated with electrolysis that has actually regrown some time later.

◇ **Inaccurate placement of probe** which puts the action of the current in the wrong area away from the matrix papilla area, having little or no effect on destruction of hair growth cells. This results in regrowth hairs 4 to 6 weeks later, depending on the area being treated.

◇ **An accurate probe with insufficient current intensity** this type of regrowth will take much longer to regrow as the whole of the lower follicle will need to be reconstructed from the remaining germinative tissue.

◇ **Insufficient length of current application time** is a common fault when treating regrowth hairs. Failing to use a high enough current intensity or apply the current application time for long enough to have maximum affect on the matrix papilla tissue, will result in a higher level of regrowth.

◇ **Missed hairs** these are the hairs that you left behind during the last treatment, either because they were too short or lying just under the skin surface, or that they were the finer lighter hairs and you concentrated on the dark, coarse, stronger and more noticeable hairgrowth first, in order to make an instant visible difference to the client.

◇ **Thinning out** the electrologist needs to advise the client that to treat all the hairs in one area in one session, would in some cases be too painful and or too damaging to the skin tissues, due to overtreating and heat convergence. The electrologist therefore treats the hairs at random, thinning them out, taking the darkest and thickest hairs first. This gives an immediate improvement to the area enabling the electrologist to thin out the finer hair growth during later sessions. This does mean, of course, that there is bound to be a percentage of regrowth and missed hairs at some stage of the treatment. However, the chances of skin damage through overworking the area are drastically reduced.

◇ **Client pain threshold** may affect your working point. Some clients prefer the flash technique, but unfortunately this usually results in a higher level of regrowth.

◇ **Skin type and sensitivity** if the skin is sensitive to the current it may result in you having to use the technique which suits the skin but which may not be ideal for the hair type. This again results in a higher regrowth than you would like.

◇ **The underlying cause of the hair growth** problem may also influence the percentage of regrowth, for example a hormonal imbalance, medication etc.

◇ **The original strength of the hairgrowth** will also influence the amount of regrowth. The electrologist needs to always check the regrowth and evaluate her technique at regular intervals if she is to maintain a high standard of workmanship. If most of your regrowth is lying deep within the follicle, then your previous probing technique was probably incorrect, too shallow, your current intensity was too low, or its application time too short.

　　If most of the regrowth is shallow it may be due to overprobing. This occurs when there are two hairs in the same follicle, the old telogen hair being visible on the skin's surface and a new anagen hair placed lower down the follicle. When probing, the electrologist by-passes the root of the telogen hair and discharges the current lower down the follicle. When epilating the old telogen hair there is only slight traction due to the follicle being shallow and the hair being ready to shed naturally soon, so probing needs to be adjusted and each hair root examined carefully when first starting treatment.

Regrowth is important to the electrologist because it helps him/her to:
◇ determine the clients next appointment due date
◇ assess the accuracy of her technique and enables her to vary it if there is a higher than expected level of regrowth.

It is possible to calculate the quantity of regrowth by always keeping a detailed record card, about how dense hairgrowth in the treatment area was at the start of a treatment course, and how long that area took you to treat. When you are positive that the true regrowth has arrived, re-treat the same hairs in that area for the second time and record how long it took you to epilate all hairgrowth this time.

　　For example if your record card had contained the following information:

'First treatment to area: worked on deep coarse hairgrowth on the front of the left lower leg, hairs mainly in early anagen. Hairgrowth not dense just long and well spaced within area, treatment time 1 hour, result mild erythema. Next week will commence first session of working on front of right lower leg.

Second treatment session to front of the lower left leg occurring six weeks later: due to the appearance of regrowth hairs when first treatment is carried out correctly. Regrowth hairs were lighter in colour, finer in texture and in the early anagen stage of the hairgrowth cycle. The time taken to cover same area was 30 minutes on this occassion.'

This would mean that your regrowth would be 50 per cent with a success rate of 50 per cent because you have worked the same area in half of the time previously taken. However if the second treatment time had only been 15 minutes of the original time taken, your regrowth would be 25 per cent with a success rate of 75 per cent.

Treatment area technique

The angle of hairgrowth on the body varies greatly between 10° and 90° depending on where the hair arises in the body and the previous method of hair removal used. Some hairs are very flat whilst others grow at a very steep angle. The electrologist needs to be very flexible in her positioning of the client and herself in order to be able to reach the various angles when probing.

Probing technique for the face

The client is positioned semi-reclined or flat, and eyepads should be offered to protect the eyes from the glare of the cold light magnifier.

Chin area

Hairs in this area vary considerably, from fine hairs lying shallow in the skin to coarse hairs with deep follicles. In some cases the tissue sheaths become excessively thickened, filling the follicle cavity completely, making probing difficult when entering the follicle. On removal of the hair a good skin stretch is required to help with swift removal as thickened sheaths offer resistance due to their size, and often make a popping noise as they leave the follicle. The angle of growth in this area varies between 45 and 90° with an average being 60°.

Top lip area

This is a very sensitive area to treat. Current intensity should be low with a shorter treatment duration of 10 to 15 minutes. Probes should be spaced out 1 in 4 or 6, according to density of hairgrowth. The hairgrowth in this area is generally fine and shallow at an angle of 45° on average. Always work from the outer corners towards the centre, thinning the centre gradually, a few hairs at a time from under the nose.

Under the chin and neck

This is a very sensitive area, with the angle of hairgrowth varying between 10° to 30° on average. Hairgrowth again will vary in type and depth of follicle, according to previous treatments and causes of hairgrowth. Sometimes probing is difficult and it is necessary to change technique. Rather than stretching the skin, pick up the tissue, ask the client to make a double chin and insert at the correct angle. This aids insertion but may feel difficult to begin with, until the technique is mastered.

The eyebrow area

This is becoming a popular area with both men and women. The follicles are usually shallow to medium in depth with coarse hairgrowth and large roots. Care must be taken when probing as skin tisues are thin and have numerous surface capillaries. If the current intensity is not high enough to cauterise blood vessels or probe too deep, bruising will result in a black eye. The skin tissues between the eyebrows have a higher moisture gradient and care is required with the current. The client lies flat and the electrologist works from the side or from behind.

The breast area

Most women develop a few hairs along the outer pigmented ring around nipple, however a small percentage develop extensive hairgrowth either in a dense circular pattern or across the entire area, whilst others develop a few hairs in between the breasts. The breast area is not as painful as most people assume, but it is advisable to avoid this area during menstruation when the breasts may be tender. Hairgrowth ranges from fine and shallow to deep and coarse, angles vary from steep to flat. A high current intensity is required due to soft fatty tissue absorbing current.

Bikini line and upper thigh

When treating this area the client should be comfortable lying either flat, on side or semi-reclined, and pillows may be used as props. This is a highly sensitive area with hairgrowth under the control of hormones as it is pubic hair. The tissue is soft and fatty with the sciatic nerve running through the area. Clients generally have a low pain threshold when treating this region. These hairs are strong and coarse in nature and are sharply angled into the skin between 45° to 90°. The probe follows the hair follicle entering the follicle mouth then flattening to progress down the follicle to its base. When hairgrowth is dense probing should be well spaced as the skin in this area is easily irritated, to prevent overtreatment of the area and tissue damage.

The underarm/axillae area

Hairgrowth in this area grows in two directions or more, generally the upper area growing upwards towards the elbow whilst the lower area grows downwards, towards the waist.

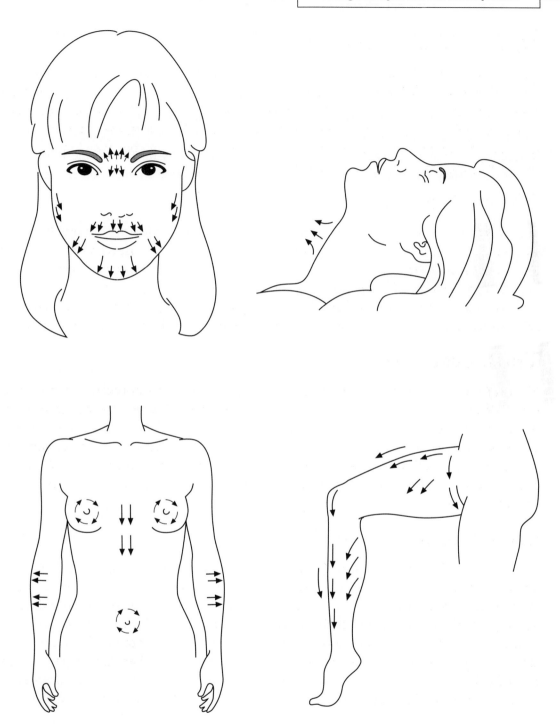

Direction of hairgrowth in various areas of the body

Deep coarse terminal hair with a well developed root structure are usually present in this area.

Abdomen

Hairgrowth direction in this area will vary either forming a circular pattern around the umbilical area or growing in an upwards direction from the bikini line. Due to the soft skin tissues in this area an extremely firm skin stretch is necessary for the needle to enter the follicle accurately. Hairs will vary in angle and nature from fine to very coarse, as the hair is pubic.

review**questions**

Q1   State six factors to be considered to ensure good probing technique.

Q2   What is the ideal heating pattern for shortwave diathermy?

Q3   Identify two disadvantages of the flash method.

Q4   List four possible causes of regrowth hairs.

Q5   State two considerations to probing technique when treating the eyebrow area.

Q6   Explain why the skin stretch is important when inserting probe into the hair follicle and removing treated hair.

Q7   Name the three factors upon which successful electrolysis technique is dependant.

Q8   Identify two types of poor probing technique which can lead to scarring of the skin tissues.

Q9   Name four factors which help you decide on the current intensity.

Q10   List and explain why increasing the current application time affects the heating pattern with short wave diathermy.

Q11   How does the moisture gradient of the skin affect short wave diathermy treatment?

Q12   The angle of hair growth on the body ranges between which degrees depending on where it arises?

Treatment methods | 9

The aim of this chapter is to introduce you to the basic science associated with electrolysis treatments and the three methods of electro-epilation, explaining the advantages and disadvantages of each. This enables you to make an informed choice when selecting the most suitable method of treatment for the skin and hair conditions presented during a consultation.

Science terminology

To understand how electrolysis works you need to have a basic understanding of science terminology.

Electricity: is energy comprising of charged particles.

Electrolysis: is the passage of a direct current through an electrolyte to bring about a chemical process.

A direct current: can be described as a steady smooth current which flows continuously in one direction only. This is achieved when there are two poles, negative and positive which enables a complete circuit to be formed. This current is used in chemical galvanic electrolysis.

An alternating oscillating current: can be described as a current which continuously changes its polarity form negative to positive. This type of current is used in short wave diathermy epilation.

High frequency: describes the number of cycles completed in one second, termed as a hertz, for example 60 hertz per second equals 60 cycles per second. This current is used in short wave diathermy epilation which combines a high frequency, oscillating alternating current.

Electrodes: are conductors which are of opposite polarities, for example a negative (cathode) and a positive (anode). Together they form a direct current circuit. When a current passes through an electrolyte solution these electrodes bring about a chemical reaction, whereby they attract ions of opposite polarity, for example the cathode, which is negatively charged, will attract cations which are positively charged. This is called anaphoresis. Whilst the anode, being positively charge attracts anions, which are negatively charged. This is called cataphoresis.

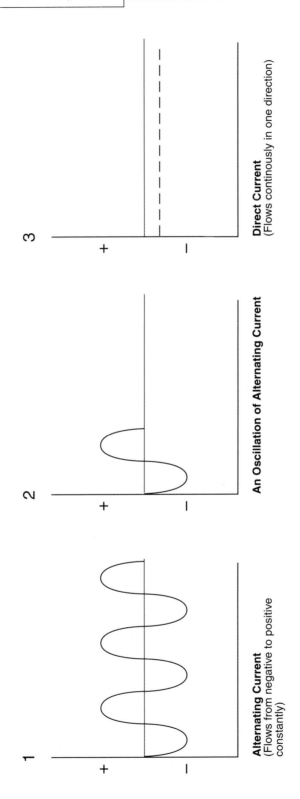

Electrical currents

1. **Alternating Current**
(Flows from negative to positive constantly)

2. **An Oscillation of Alternating Current**

3. **Direct Current**
(Flows continously in one direction)

An electrolyte: is a solution which conducts electricity by allowing the passage of ions to flow through it. The hair follicle and skin tissues are a natural electrolyte.

Molecules: are simple units of matter composed of two or more atoms.

Atoms: are the smallest part of matter. Atoms have a central nucleus around which negatively charged electrons rotate. Contained within its nucleus are protons which are positively charged particles and neutrons which have no charge. They join up with each other to form molecules.

Ions: are formed when an atom loses or gains an electron from its outer shell. These ions may be either negatively charged called anions or positively charged called cations.

A conductor: allows the passage of electrons as an electrical current, for example water or copper etc.

Insulator: prevents the passage of electricity, for example rubber or plastic etc.

Electrons: are negatively charged particles that form the part of the atom outside the nucleus.

Protons: are the nucleus of all atoms, carrying a positive charge of electricity.

A rectifier: changes an alternating current from the mains circuit to a direct current by allowing current to flow in one direction only.

A transformer: is a device to change the voltage of an alternating current by either increasing or decreasing its voltage.

A capacitor/condenser: stores an electrical charge.

A rheostat: varies the current flowing in a circuit, for example the stronger the current the lower the resistance.

Galvanic chemical epilation

This is the oldest form of epilation and uses a direct current which possesses polarity because it flows in one direction only through a circuit. To achieve this the current needs one negative and one positive electrode for a circuit to be completed. It works on the principle of producing a movement of ions in the skin tissues from negative to positive, or visa versa. This also can be called electrolysis.

During galvanic chemical epilation/electrolysis the client is connected to the anode which they hold in their hand. This is then connected to the positive outlet on the electrolysis machine, whilst the needle electrode is connected to the negative outlet on the machine and therefore negatively charged.

The needle is inserted into the hair follicle which contains a natural electrolyte, water (H_2O) and salt (Sodium Chloride NaCl). This leads to increased conductivity of the skin tissues allowing the current to flow readily through the skin. As the direct current passes through the tissues it causes a chemical chain reaction to occur. This results in the atoms of the salt and water breaking down. The atoms split into negatively and positively charged ions, called cations and anions, that rearrange themselves to form new chemical substances, sodium hydroxide at the cathode and hydrochloric acid at the anode.

The chemical structure of water is 2 hydrogen atoms (H_2O) and 1 oxygen atom (O_2), whilst the chemical structure of salt is 1 sodium atom (NaCl) and 1 chloride atom (Cl). During electrolysis these chemicals simply separate into sodium ions and chloride ions, all the ions produced usually pair up immediately, as they are unstable in this format, so the chloride ions join together to form chlorine gas (Cl_2). Whilst the hydrogen ions pair up to form hydrogen gas (H_2), this leaves the sodium ion (Na) to pair up with the hydroxy ion (OH) thus forming the chemical sodium hydroxide (NaOH) at the cathode. Sodium hydroxide also known as lye is a highly caustic alkali which is available along the whole length of the needle. It is able to penetrate the skin tissues and curved follicles due to its wide treatment pattern. This results in tissue destruction through chemical decomposition of the lower follicle, where the moisture is more concentrated, either rendering the follicles inactive or weakening its ability to reproduce new hairgrowth.

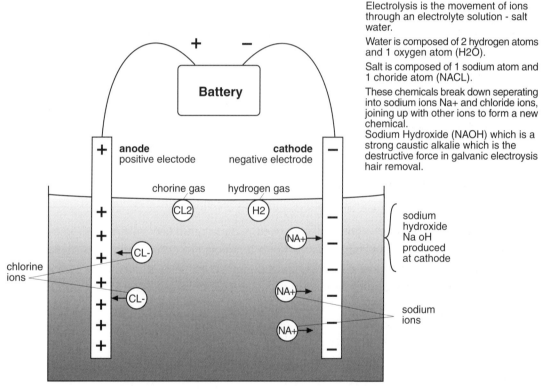

Electrolysis is the movement of ions through an electrolyte solution - salt water.

Water is composed of 2 hydrogen atoms and 1 oxygen atom (H2O).

Salt is composed of 1 sodium atom and 1 choride atom (NACL).

These chemicals break down seperating into sodium ions Na+ and chloride ions, joining up with other ions to form a new chemical.

Sodium Hydroxide (NAOH) which is a strong caustic alkalie which is the destructive force in galvanic electroysis hair removal.

Electrolysis the chemical process

This chemical reaction is not immediate but takes time to build up and depends on three factors:
✧ how high the current intensity is
✧ how long the current application time is
✧ the moisture level within the tissues.

Fine hairgrowth may require up to 10 seconds or more on a low current intensity, whereas deep, coarse terminal hairgrowth may require a higher intensity of current for 20 or 30 seconds leading up to several minutes of treatment, for treatment to be effective in producing sufficient lye. The treatment does not cease when the current stops as the chemical action continues to build up within the tissues for a short time afterwards (just like switching on a fire your room is not instantly heated, it takes time for the heat to build up in the room). Therefore, leave the hair *in situ* for a few minutes while you treat other similar hairs in the area, before removing it, hence up to several minutes treatment time. Always refer to manufacturer's instructions. Occasionally hydrogen gas will appear as froth on the skin surface. This is a by-product of the treatment which is harmless to the skin, but should be wiped off to prevent the current from travelling onto the skin surface. At the anode another gas may be released called chlorine gas, which combines with water and forms hydrochloric acid and is distributed over the electrode surface, without causing any irritation normally.

The advantages of galvanic electrolysis are:
✧ Ideal for distorted follicles as sodium hydroxide is able to penetrate curved follicles due to its wide treatment pattern
✧ Able to treat deep, coarse terminal hairgrowth more effectively than short wave diathermy
✧ The current is concentrated in the lower follicle due to the moisture levels being greater here and the sebum insulating the upper drier, skin surface tissues
✧ Regrowth is less than short wave diathermy, but more than the blend method, due to the sodium hydroxide not being heated by the high frequency current with this method
✧ This method can be used on nervous clients.

The disadvantages of galvanic electrolysis are:
✧ Not ideally suited to fine shallow hairgrowth
✧ Requires more time than short diathermy treatment
✧ Fewer hairs can be treated in one session than with short wave diathermy, due to length of treatment time for individual hairs.

Short wave diathermy

Also known as:
✧ thermolysis,
✧ high frequency,
✧ radio frequency (R.F.)(uses short wave band)

This method superseded galvanic epilation during the 1930's, due to the speed of treatment. Short wave diathermy uses a high frequency oscillating, alternating current that produces thermal heat as its destructive force. This current is directed through a fine steel needle into the matrix/dermal papilla area of the hair follicle and is discharged for 2–3 seconds approximately.

The high frequency current is constantly changing direction and polarity from negative to positive. The energy produced is absorbed by the water molecules in the cells at the base of the follicle and its effect is to generate friction through agitating the tissues, which creates thermal heat. This heat is produced at the needle tip in a pear/teardrop pattern, which breaks down the cellular structure by causing the proteins in the cells to congeal. Coagulation and cauterisation of the blood vessels in the area, results in either rendering the follicle inactive or weakening its ability to reproduce new hairgrowth. The surface skin tissues should not be affected if correct treatment procedures and techniques are used.

The advantages of short wave diathermy are:
✧ It is the quickest method of semi-permanent hair removal, as an increased number of hairs can be treated within a short period of time when compared to the blend or galvanic methods
✧ The skin heals fairly quickly after treatment.

The disadvantages of short wave diathermy are:
✧ It is ineffective in treating curved and distorted hair follicles
✧ There is a high level of regrowth generally
✧ Overall length of treatment course is longer.

The blend method

This method became very popular during the 1990's in English clinics/salons, but had been widely used abroad prior to that time, due to its effectiveness in treating any type of hair follicle, including the most difficult, distorted follicles as the treatment pattern was wide and deep.

The blend is a combination of both short wave diathermy and galvanic electrolysis. It utilises the best of each current, the thoroughness of galvanic with the speed of short wave diathermy, to produce a really effective and efficient method of removing superfluous hairgrowth, long term. Both currents are available either individually or together, which enables treatments to be tailored to client's individual needs, as there are several techniques available with the blend method to the electrologist. Regrowth is minimal but treatment time is longer than short wave diathermy, at around 5 seconds a hair.

With the blend method there is a minimal amount of short wave diathermy current used. Its function is to produce thermal heat, to warm the lye as it is produced within the follicle by the galvanic current, therefore the destructive force of the blend is heated lye (sodium hydroxide). The effect of heating the lye is to speed up the chemical action making it more caustic and destructive, the skin tissues are more receptive and the lye seeps readily into any area. The result is chemical decomposition of the lower hair follicle.

Thus rendering the follicle inactive or weakening its ability to reproduce hairgrowth. There is minimal regrowth compared with using either galvanic or short wave diathermy currents on their own, if the treatment is carried out correctly. There are a variety of blend machines available on the market today. Most manufactures offer additional training and written instructions to which you should always refer, to enable you to provide the best possible treatment to your clientele. 'Sterex' are particularly helpful in this area offering training to individuals, colleges and training centres alike.

With the blend method care is needed when blending the currents. If too much galvanic current is used it will offset the action of the short wave diathermy, reducing the heating effect making the skin tissues less receptive to the lye, and leading to weeping follicles due to overtreatment by the galvanic current. Whilst too much short wave diathermy would result in less galvanic action, insufficient lye production, cauterisation of the germinal/matrix area will possibly lead to surface tissue damage, depending on depth of probe and amount of short wave diathermy used.

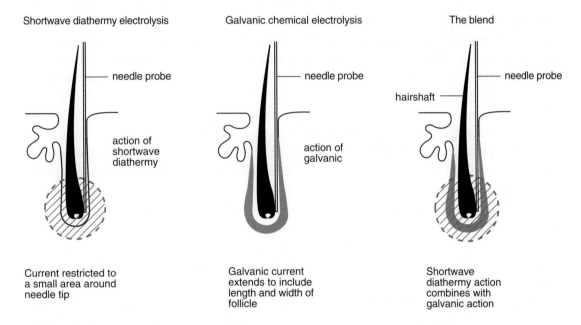

Shortwave diathermy electrolysis

needle probe

action of
shortwave
diathermy

Current restricted to
a small area around
needle tip

Galvanic chemical electrolysis

needle probe

action of
galvanic

Galvanic current
extends to include
length and width of
follicle

The blend

hairshaft

needle probe

Shortwave
diathermy action
combines with
galvanic action

Treatment field comparisons between electrolysis methods

The advantages of the blend method are:

✧ There is minimal regrowth as heated lye is more effective in destroying skin tissue
✧ Treatment can be individually tailored to clients skin and hair type, due the versatility of the blend method

✧ Generally thought to be less painful than either short wave diathermy or galvanic generally

✧ More effective than either galvanic or short wave diathermy on their own.

Disadvantages of the blend method are:

✧ Takes longer than short wave diathermy

✧ May cost more for treatment as the equipment is more expensive for the electrologist to purchase and it takes more time to deliver treatment.

The blend procedure

This is similar to the galvanic method. The client is connected to the anode electrode whilst the needle is the active, cathode electrode. The electrologist sets application time to 5 seconds on average and sets the current intensity dials for short wave diathermy and the blend to a minimum as instructed by the manufacturers. The needle is inserted into the hair follicle and the current is discharged either via a finger or foot switch, for the full 5 seconds. Generally the hair will not come out as the current intensity settings are on minimum. The electrologist therefore increases the intensity of the galvanic current until the hair epilates readily without traction. Having established this, most hairs of a similar nature in that area should be able to be treated. However, when moving to a new area there may be a need to modify the current intensity levels according to hair type, skin reaction and client pain threshold. Some electrologists use the 'treat and leave' method, where, having established the correct current intensities, you treat a hair and leave it in the follicle whilst you continue to work in the area on a group of 6 to 10 hairs of a similar nature, returning to remove the hairs left behind, having allowed them to continue to be treated by the lye for a short while after the current has stopped. This occurs as the chemical action takes time to build up within the tissues, before being neutralised by the skin's ph level. I personally find this method very effective for both myself and the client as it allows for speed of treatment and client comfort.

review questions

Q1   State and explain which method of electrolysis is most suited to a client with fine shallow hairgrowth on the top lip.

Q2   Name two chemicals produced during galvanic electrolysis.

Q3   Briefly explain the role of high frequency within the blend method of electrolysis.

Q4   What is the other alternative term used to describe sodium hydroxide?

Q5   Which method of electrolysis is best suited to treat deep coarse textured hair-growth on the chin which has previously been shaved.

Q6   What type of current is used with galvanic chemical electrolysis?

Q7   Describe how thermal heat is produced during short wave diathermy electrolysis.

Q8   What is the effect of thermal heat on the skin tissues during electrolysis?

Q9   State two disadvantages of short wave diathermy.

Q10 Identify three advantages of the blend method of electrolysis.

Q11 State two advantages of galvanic electrolysis.

Q12 Which method of electrolysis is active along the entire length of the needle?

Alternative methods of hair removal | 10

This chapter introduces you to a range of hair removal methods available on the market today, some have been around for many years, whilst others are relatively new technology which, when compared to electrolysis, have yet to be tried and tested long-term. As with many new forms of technology and medicines the long term effects are not always known for some twenty years. It is, therefore, essential that you have an understanding of as many methods of hair removal as possible, in order to make an informed choice when selecting or recommending suitable methods of hair removal to clients, for either short-term or long-term success, and to match skin type and hair type etc, to the most appropriate treatment. Many clients are now looking for a fast method of hair removal, either short-term or long-term, which does not require a prolonged commitment of time, as does electrolysis. As a professional you should be able to discuss alternative methods of hair removal, their advantages and disadvantages, and offer a choice of methods. Remember electrolysis is not for everyone.

Short-term methods of hair removal

These are methods which are effective from a few days to a couple months, and give a quick instant result.
✦ Shaving
✦ Plucking
✦ Cutting
✦ Abrasives
✦ Depilatory creams
✦ Threading
✦ Sugaring
✦ Waxing.

Shaving: this is a quick, cheap and effective method of hair removal, that removes hairgrowth from the surface of the skin only, blunting the hairgrowth. Within 48 hours stubble is either seen or felt depending on the hair type. Most people find that over a period of time hairgrowth becomes coarser and darker than the original growth. The skin tissues may also be adversely affected. It can be be irritated and there may also be cuts from poor technique which in some cases may result in scar tissue formation.

Plucking: this method of hair removal is only suitable for small areas of hairgrowth, for example eyebrows. Each individual hair is treated by being plucked in the direction of its growth, which is time consuming when compared to either shaving, waxing, pulsed light or laser therapy. If used regularly on the chin or top lip it can lead to pigmentation problems and infected follicles, and should therefore not be recommended for those areas. Regrowth is from 6 to 12 weeks depending on stage of growth and type of hair etc. Plucking does damage the hair follicle as it generally leads to a distorted follicle forming.

Cutting: this is the use of small scissors to cut the hairgrowth to skin level. This is an acceptable method of controlling unwanted hairgrowth between electrolysis treatments. There are no adverse effects on the hairgrowth as the hair root and skin tissues are not affected. The hair tip just becomes blunt.

Abrasives: these may be pumice stones or abrasive gloves which mechanicallly produce friction when rubbed across the skin tissues in a circular motion. This causes the hair to break off from the skin's surface. Regrowth occurs usually within a few days. Skin tissues may show an initial irritation depending on the product used, frequency and duration of use.

Depilatory cream: these are strong alkaline chemical based products with a ph range of between 10–12.5 which attacks the molecular structure of the hair. It may contain either the chemical calcium thioglycollate, calcium hydroxide or strontium sulphide which break down the keratin protein within the hairshaft, after approximately 10 minutes, depending on the chemical involved. It is showered or wiped off the skin's surface with the spatula. This strong caustic action often leads to hyper-pigmentation of the skin tissues and skin irritation which with prolonged and regular use can cause an allergic reaction, for example dermatitis. Regrowth is usually within one to two weeks.

Threading: this is when a piece of cotton thread is wrapped around the fingers and then twisted in rapid movements to and fro, across the skin. The twisted cotton thread plucks the hairs rapidly by frictional abrasion, catching hold of the hairs. This may result in the possible distortion of the follicles, as plucking is not with the direction of hairgrowth. Regrowth varies from a few days to several weeks depending of the skill of the operator and hairgrowth cycle.

Sugaring: this is a method of hair removal originating in the Middle East and uses pure natural products that contain no chemicals or additives. It is relatively cheap and gives quick instant results. The sugar paste is a mixture of water, glucose or fructose syrup (sugar) and lemon juice which is boiled until a caramelised paste is formed. The paste is then rolled onto the skin where it sticks to the hair. It is removed quickly taking the hairgrowth with it, rather like waxing. Regrowth is on average between 6–8 weeks depending on skill of the operator and the hairgrowth cycle. The disadvantage of this method is ingrowing hairs may result.

Waxing: this is, in my opinion, the best short-term method of hair removal as it is able to treat large areas of hairgrowth for between 6–8 weeks very successfully. Regrowth is soft when compared to shaving and there is no adverse skin reaction, generally only an initial erythema.

There are two methods using hot and warm wax. This allows one to treat each client according to hair and skin type with the most appropriate method.

Hot wax: is a blend of bee's wax and resins which are heated to a temperature of approximately 48°–68°, according to manufacturer's instructions. It is then applied using a spatula against the direction of hairgrowth where is sets rapidly and is then quickly ripped off rather like a plaster, against the direction of hairgrowth, removing the hairs. It is ideal for coarse dark hairgrowth as the heat helps to open the follicles and allow hairgrowth to be removed easily from the follicle.

Warm wax: is a honey, glucose or fructose syrup (sugar) base which may contain additives according to the make, which is heated to between 38°–43° and then applied in the direction of hairgrowth with a spatula. A paper or material strip is then moulded to the wax and ripped quickly off against the direction of hairgrowth. This method is ideal for sensitive skin due to the lower temperature, and suits most people.

Wax pot

Alternative methods of long-term hair removal

These new, long-term, methods of hair removal include the following:
✧ laser therapy
✧ intense pulsed light therapy.

These are methods which use relatively new technology in the field of hair removal, and have been the most controversial to date, with some manufacturers making unsubstantiated claims regarding their amazing success. To highlight the controversy, in July 2000 a paper from the 'Washington Institute of Dermatological Laser Surgery' said 'None of the currently approved (laser) systems can yet be said to induce permanent hair loss'. This controversy will continue until long-term trials over many years have documented evidence to the effectiveness of laser therapy's ability to remove hair permanently, preferably under medical supervision.

In America the definition of long-term hair removal, is that of reduced hairgrowth of 3 months duration or more. In February 2000, the FDA (Food and Drug Administration) gave clearance for one manufacturer of hair removal systems to advertise that hair removal is permanent, if hair removal is achieved when there is a long-term stable reduction in the number of regrowing hairs. This must be over a time greater than the duration of the complete growth cycle of the hair follicle, for example 3 to 12 months or longer, depending on the area treated. Regardless of the fact that this is new technology and no one knows how long hairgrowth reduction will last, be it 3 months, 3 years or 13 years. It is far too early to say permanent hair loss has been achieved as these treatment are so new, and have not been proven over many years. On the other hand electrolysis has been around since 1875 and has been tried, tested and proven, when used by skilled and experienced electrologists. However, in England, we state that we can offer a long-term reduction in hairgrowth to improve the quality of our client's lifestyle, when using any form of long-term hair removal system. In my opinion there is a place for this new technology alongside electrolysis in clinics and salons for many years to come. This new technology is not suitable for everyone and is expensive. Given time, laser and intense pulsed light therapy will become more efficient and less expensive, as technology improves it generally becomes more affordable to both the operator and clients.

The electromagnetic spectrum

The spectrum is made up of a variety of wavelengths, which include both visible and invisible light rays, producing radiation that can be both beneficial and harmful to the skin tissues. The visible light spectrum (white light) is composed of seven colours, violet, indigo, blue, green, yellow, orange and red. The colour of light is determined by its wavelength, for example short

The Electromagnetic Spectrum

Type of wave	X-rays & gamma rays	Ultra-violet			Visible light							Infra-red		Radio
		UVC	UVB	UVA	V	I	B	G	Y	O	R	short	long	
Wave length	100nm	280nm	315nm	400nm	500nm		600nm				700nm	1200	1400nm	1mm
	Short													Long
Frequency	High														Low
Description		Cold invisible rays			Visible rays							Warm invisible rays		
Skin penetration		superficial epidermis	deep epidermis	blood vessels of dermis	subcutaneous							superficial epidermis		
Sun's radiation at Earth's surface														

laser

IPL

Key
IPL - intense pulsed light 500 - 1200 nm
Laser - 694 - 1064
nm - nano metres

infra red rays are of a shorter wave length covering a broad band of the electromagnetic spectrum between 700–1400nm. These electromagnetic waves carry energy which both the lasers and intense pulsed light units are able to use as their destructive source, depending on the equipment design. Infra red rays are able to penetrate the skin tissues quite deeply between 3–5mm, with their energy being absorbed by the skin's molecules ie, water, melanin or blood which cause these molecules to vibrate rapidly and generate heat within the skin tissue targeted (hair follicles), thus producing a rise in skin temperature.

Glossary

Laser: light amplification by stimulated emission of radiation.
Photo-thermolysis: light is used as the destructive force of laser and intense pulsed light units, to produce thermal heat and destroy germinative tissue.
Nano-metre: is one millionth of a millimetre.
Photons: particles of light energy.
Selective thermolysis: short bursts of intense light of variable wavelengths.
Fluence: is the amount of energy going into the skin tissues by centimetres squared, for example 3.0 joules per cm.
Chromophores: refer to any moleculer which absorbs light, for example melanin, blood etc.
Coherence: inherent synchronity, laser light is both spatially and temporally coherent, one colour in phase and parallel.
Collimation: parallelity of light.
Monochromaticity: single colour and all waves one length.
Chromatic: coloured.
Divergence: refers to the angle that light spreads from source.
Coherent monochromatic, collimated device: is a laser which uses a parallel fixed single wave of one colour.
Wavelength: is the distance between two points on the wave, which are separated by one complete cycle.
Pulse Duration: the length of time the laser/intense pulse light is applied to the skin tissues varies from one billionth of a second up to several thousandths of a second according to manufacture.
Spot size: is where the laser beam falls onto the skin tissues and is measured in millimetres.

The principle of laser therapy

Laser therapy has been used in the medical field since the early 1960's to treat a wide range of conditions, from vascular conditions, for example portwine stains, eye conditions such as cataracts, some forms of cancer, to physiotherapy.

However, it was only during the 1990's that laser therapy has been directed towards the management or elimination of unwanted hairgrowth, with its introduction to a limited number of clinics and salons by doctors from about 1998.

Lasers are coherent, monochromatic, collimated devices, which simply means laser therapy is the use of a parallel, fixed, single wavelength or colour (visible red to infra red) in pulses at 645 nanometres. These waves can be absorbed by one particular colour or material, whilst being reflected from any other colour or material. They are waves also able to penetrate the skin tissues to a depth of 0.14mm.

There are many types of laser equipment available on the market and they are classified by the laser medium they use, (see chart 'types of lasers').

A brief explanation of a laser treatment procedure is that a cooling gel is applied evenly to an area, then the selected laser beam scans the skin tissues within the treatment area targeting the melanin pigment found within the cortex of the hair shaft. Short even bursts of light energy pulses are delivered which generate thermal heat. This is absorbed by the pigment melanin within hairshaft and follicles, causing desiccation to the hairshaft and coagulation to surrounding follicular tissue. This is said to either reduce or destroy the follicle's ability to reproduce hairgrowth.

To date, there have been varying degrees of success in the treatment of unwanted hairgrowth by lasers. It appears more successful on fair skins with dark hairgrowth, and less successful on blonde or white hairgrowth, which has proven resistant probably due to lack of melanin density. However, there have been some unwanted side effects, such as blistering of skin tissues and hyper-pigmentation of tissues, particularly with dark skin types.

The Ruby and Alexandrite lasers use a wavelength between 694–755 nanometers generally. The laser beam is passed over the treatment area for a fraction of a second (one thousandth) in an attempt to weaken or destroy the follicle's ability to reproduce hairgrowth. This type of laser was one of the first to have any success in treating hair removal although limited to dark pigmented hair on fair skin. It was initially, however, unsuccessful on darker pigmented skin tissues, producing blistering and hypo-pigmentation marks, and having no real success on blonde hairgrowth. At the present time, trials with the Alexandrite laser are being carried out in England at the Royal Free Hospital, by Dr William Clayton on patients suffering with unwanted hairgrowth as a result of hormonal imbalance from the condition polycystic ovaries syndrome (PCOS).

In America, there has been one case reported of increased hairgrowth following the use of a Ruby laser. This occurred in Los Angeles when, after treatment, it was found that two hairs started growing from one follicle (multigemini) on a client previously thought to be an ideal candidate for laser treatment. According to Dr Ye of Los Angeles 'it is hypothesized that the light energy of the laser was not enough to destroy the hair follicles in this case, instead of destroying them it activated them from the sleeping phase (telogen) (reference Dermatology Times). However, at present there appear to be no other similar reports recorded. This does mean that further research is needed into the long-term effects.

Chart of Laser and Intensive Pulsed Light Units Available

Amplifying Medium	Wavelength	Colour	Brand Name	Fluence Energy	Pulse Width	Spot Size
Ruby Laser	694nm	Red	Chromos	5–20 J/cm	1 ms	7mm
Alexandrite Laser	755nm	Red	Gentle Lase	6–100J/cm	3 ms	8–18mm
Nd YAG Laser	1064nm	IR	Softlight	2,5J/cm	10 ms	7mm
	1064nm	IR	Biolase	14–200 J/cm	1–10 ms	7/12mm
	1064nm	IR	Smart Epil	11–90 J/cm	5 ms	6 mm
	1064nm	IR	Depilase	5–200 J/cm	5–50 ms	4–6 mm
Diode Laser	808nm	IR	Visulase	0.8–500 J/cm	15–999 ms	1.5 mm
	800nm	IR	Light Sheer	10–40 J/cm		
	810nm	IR	Quartet	0–30 J/cm	5 ms–3s	2.5 mm
	809nm	IR	Scanda Red			1.3 mm
Flash Lamp IPLS	500–1200nm	Red IR	Epilight	0–65 J/cm	8–12 ms	8×35/10×45
	645–1200nm	Red IR	Aestilight	20–40 J/cm	3×4 ms	10×20 mm
	620–950nm	Red IR	Skinsoft	3–45 J/cm	15–40 ms	5 cm
	650–1100nm	Red IR	Depilight	50 J/cm	1–5 ms	3 cm
	600–920nm	Red IR	Plasmalight	100 J/cm	1–100 ms	10×20 mm
	695–1200nm	Red IR	Aculight	25–40 J/cm	16–315 ms	8×34 mm
	+645 Filter					
	+755–1200nm filter					
	600–950nm	Red IR	Ellipse	6–21 J/cm	10–40 ms	10×48 mm
	600–959nm	Red IR	Beaulight	3–45 J/cm	15–40 ms	5 cm
	400–1200nm	Red IR	Spa Touch	2–7.5 J/cm	35 ms	22×55 mm

The second generation of lasers include the new diode laser, which uses infrared colour at a fixed wavelength of 808 nanometres. This is said to have addressed some of the problems experienced with the Ruby and Alexandrite lasers, namely that they are able to treat a broader range of skin and hair types.

The diode laser scans the treatment area emitting a short but even burst of light energy for a fraction of a second, this generates thermal heat which is absorbed by both the pigment melanin in the hairshaft and the blood vessels in the hair bulb/papilla region of the hair follicles within the field of the beam, causing destruction or damage to the hair follicles. The hair is either destroyed immediately or falls out within seven days on average.

Laser Classification

There are four classes of laser which have been internationally agreed upon based on the potential danger posed to the skin and eyes.

Class 1: refers to low power lasers which use both the visible and invisible wavelengths of the electromagnetic spectrum. Lasers within this classification pose no immediate danger to the skin and eyes as they are enclosed systems which do not emit hazardous levels of radiation, for example low output HE-NE and semi-conductor diode lasers.

Class 2: refers to low-power lasers in the visible wavelength of the electromagnetic spectrum. Lasers within this classification are considered safe for extended periods of irradiation on unprotected skin tissues. However it is not advisable to view directly into the path of the beam due to the brilliance of these visible lasers, for example HE-NE with outputs of up to 1mw.

Class 3: refers to mid-powered lasers using both visible and invisible wavelengths of the electromagnetic spectrum and are considered to be potentially harmful to the eyes, but not the skin. Therefore protective goggles must be worn when using lasers within this classification. The radiant output of lasers within this class range is from 1mw to 500mw.

Class 4: refers to high powered lasers which are very harmful to both unprotected skin and eyes. They pose a fire hazard and are used for surgery, for example CO_2 lasers and Argon lasers.

Soft light method

This method requires regular treatments at intervals, several times a year to achieve long term reduction in hairgrowth, offering a quicker alternative to electrolysis treatments.

Soft light uses a low energy (2.5 joules per cm squared) class 2 Nd:YAG laser with a near infra red fixed wavelength (giving a sensation of heat within the tissues) which targets a black carbon solution which has previously been applied to waxed skin tissues and allowed to absorb into the hair follicles, where it deposits carbon particles. Excess on the skin's surface is then removed and a cooling gel wiped onto the surface tissues. Then the laser is scanned across the skin tissues quickly, emitting pulses of light where it targets the carbon solution (as laser is tuned to carbon particle frequency), delivering a short burst of energy-heat to the base of the hair follicles within the treatment field. This vaporises the carbon lotion within the hair follicle, causing the skin and follicle tissue around the carbon particles to coagulate and weakens the hair follicle's ability to reproduce hair. Any regrowth hairs will be slower to regrow, being lighter in colour and finer in texture.

A large area of hairgrowth can be treated in one session. There is no damage to the skin tissues surrounding the hair follicles as the laser targets only the carbon deposits. However, hyper-pigmentation can occur in some cases. Trials to date reportedly show after a year, a 40 per cent reduction in hairgrowth in clients who have had a course of treatments.

Contra-indications to soft light hair removal

✧ Pregnancy
✧ Diabetes
✧ Previous exposure to sunlight, excluded for 6 weeks after exposure
✧ Medication which causes photo-sensitization
✧ Aromatherapy oils, some cause photo-sensitization
✧ St. John's Wort users
✧ Vascular disorders
✧ Acne drug users
✧ Clients with cancer history
✧ Epilepsy
✧ Lack of skin sensation
✧ Pigmentation disorders
✧ Keloid scar sufferers
✧ Herpes simplex (cold sore)
✧ Liver and kidney disorders
✧ Multiple sclerosis
✧ Migraine sufferers
✧ Heart disorders
✧ Hair lighter than skin depending on equipment
✧ Eyebrows, due to thinness of skin tissues
✧ Skin infections and diseases
✧ Bruising
✧ Abrasions.

Home care advice

✧ No sunbathing, for 48 hours after treatment a sun protection cream is recommended with a spf factor of 15+
✧ Do not interfere with hairgrowth in between treatments.

Average treatment times and costs will vary greatly with each operator and method used. Below is a guide to treatment times and cost that are current in 2001 at the time of writing.

Area	Time	Price
Upper lip	15 minutes	£125
Chin	20 minutes	£150–£250
Bikini line	45 minutes	£250–£350
Legs	90 minutes	£1000–£1200
Abdomen	30 minutes	£200–£300
Backs	30–90 minutes	£400–£800

The Principle of intense pulsed light therapy

This works on the same principle as laser therapy using selective photo-thermolyis and is an advanced version of laser therapy.

Intense pulsed light is a non-invasive treatment which uses non parallel light waves of variable length (not in phase) which are controlled by a filter, to remove the harmful light colours of blue, green, yellow and orange, selecting only the visible red or infrared light waves. This results in using a much broader range of wavelengths of between 500–1200 nanometres, which are able to penetrate the skin tissues to a depth of between 3–7mm depending on equipment used, and can be customised to meet the individual's skin and hair type.

Intense pulsed light emits precise flashs of light radiation (across the treatment area which can be very large or small due to a range of different filter head sizes available), which are absorbed by the chromophore, in this case the melanin pigment within the hairshaft. The skin is prepared for treatment with hairgrowth clipped, followed by a cleansing application, then a cooling gel is applied over the skin tissues between 1–2 mm thick, to reduce skin surface reaction. The correct filter size is selected for the size of the treatment area and wavelength required (see chart on filters). Then intense pulsed light is applied evenly in short bursts of light energy, targeting the pigment melanin in the hairshaft, which absorbs the light radiation and converts it into thermal heat. The pigment cells become excited and vibrate, generating heat within the tissues, damaging or destroying them by photo-thermolysis. This causes vaporisation and coagulation to surrounding follicular tissue, either reducing or destroying the hair follicles ability to reproduce hairgrowth.

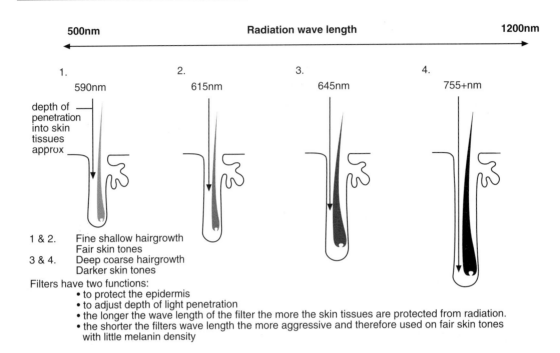

| 500nm | Radiation wave length | 1200nm |

1.   2.   3.   4.

590nm   615nm   645nm   755+nm

depth of penetration into skin tissues approx

1 & 2.   Fine shallow hairgrowth
         Fair skin tones
3 & 4.   Deep coarse hairgrowth
         Darker skin tones

Filters have two functions:
- to protect the epidermis
- to adjust depth of light penetration
- the longer the wave length of the filter the more the skin tissues are protected from radiation.
- the shorter the filters wave length the more aggressive and therefore used on fair skin tones with little melanin density

Filter choice

The light energy emitted is so quick, being only a fraction of a second, it is thought that the nerves within the tissue do not have time to respond, hence the claim by some manufacturers and clients that the treatment is pain free. However, each individual's pain threshold is variable, and therefore this claim is subjective.

Intense pulse light units have pre-set skin and hair type programmes, to help prevent or limit the risk of skin damage such as hyper-pigmentation etc (manual override is also available for the experienced therapist.) This makes allowances for, and automatically changes, the energy or fluence level and the delay between pulses, for example the darker the pigment of the skin and hair, the lower the fluence (energy) and the more pulses, with longer delays between each pulse. This delay factor is to prevent skin tissues overheating, as the hair is able to retain the heat over the pulse time, and for longer than the thin tissue of the epidermis. Fine light hair requires a high fluence with less pulses and a short delay factor, usually requiring more treatment sessions due to less melanin present in the hairshaft to absorb light and less thermal heat generated within the hair follicle. The finer the hair and darker the hairgrowth, the quicker the treatment and lower the fluence. Intense pulsed light works more effectively on dark coarse textured early anagen hairs. Where the hair follicles are shorter and the amount of melanin pigment generally higher in density, and cells are active, then the absorption level is greater. It is not a suitable treatment for someone who is even slightly suntanned, as the intense pulse light is unable to differentiate between the

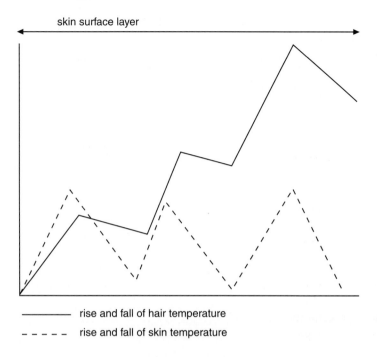

skin surface layer

—————— rise and fall of hair temperature

– – – – – rise and fall of skin temperature

The effect of intense pulsed light on temperature of hair and skin

melanin in the hairshaft and skin tissues. There is therefore a risk of hypo- or hyper-pigmentation occurring. However, this method can be used on Asian and Black skins but great care is required when treating them to prevent hyper-pigmentation occurring permanently. A test patch should enable the therapist to make appropriate adaptations to minimise any risks of skin damage.

Factors to consider when customising treatment to suit an individual's needs
✧ Skin type
✧ Skin colour
✧ Hairgrowth density
✧ Hair type and follicle depth
✧ Hair colour
✧ Energy fluence level
✧ Pulse mode
✧ Pulse duration
✧ Filter size and wavelength.

Contra-indications to intense pulsed light
✧ Pregnancy
✧ Diabetes

✧ Previous exposure to sunlight, excluded for 6 weeks after exposure
✧ Medication which causes photo-sensitization
✧ Aromatherapy oils, some cause photo-sensitization
✧ St. John's Wort users
✧ Vascular disorders
✧ Acne drug users
✧ Clients with cancer history
✧ Epilepsy
✧ Lack of skin sensation
✧ Pigmentation disorders
✧ Keloid scar sufferers
✧ Herpes simplex (cold sore)
✧ Liver and kidney disorders
✧ Multiple sclerosis
✧ Migraine sufferers
✧ Heart disorders
✧ Hair lighter than skin depending on manufacturer
✧ Eyebrows, due to thinness of skin tissues
✧ Skin infections and diseases
✧ Bruising
✧ Abrasions.

Skin reactions to intense pulsed light

✧ Mild erythema
✧ Localised swelling
✧ An adverse reaction would be hypo-pigmentation
✧ An adverse reaction would be hyper-pigmentation
✧ Bruising in vascular areas, for example bikini lines
✧ Occasional blistering and indication that treatment requires modifying.

Post-treatment advice

✧ Application of sunblock for 14 days after treatment
✧ Application of an appropriate moisturiser daily
✧ Avoid exposure to sunlight whilst having treatment course
✧ If skin tissues are uncomfortable apply cold compress after treatment
✧ Advise on date of next treatment.

Skin type categories for laser and intense pulsed light

The Fitzpatrick skin type categories appear to be the guidelines used by most manufactures of laser and intense pulse light therapy treatments.

Skin type i	always burns and never tans.
Skin type ii	always burns and sometimes tans.
Skin type iii	sometimes burns but always tans.
Skin type iv	rarely burns but always tans.
Skin type v	moderately pigmented skins.
Skin type vi	Black skin (Afro-Caribbean).

reviewquestions

Q1 List three common methods of short-term hair removal.

Q2 Name two new technology, long-term methods of hair removal.

Q3 State what time period the FDA define as long-term hair removal.

Q4 Name two types of lasers which can, or have been, used for hair removal treatment.

Q5 State three things which can cause photo-sensitization as a contra-indication to laser or intense pulsed light therapy.

Q6 List four factors to consider when customising treatment to meet a client's individual needs.

Q7 State two possible unwanted side effects of laser therapy.

Q8 State why blonde or white hair is probably resistant to laser and intense pulsed light therapy.

Q9 Name the class of laser which does not damage either the eyes or skin tissues.

Q10 List four types of possible skin reactions to intense pulsed light therapy.

Q11 Name two types of natural chromophores which absorb light.

Q12 State two functions of the filter used in laser and intense pulsed light therapy.

Post-treatment advice and problems | 11

This chapter introduces you to the post-treatment care, and advice that a client should receive and possible adverse reactions to electrolysis treatment. It is essential that you have an understanding of this in order to take every precaution to prevent unnecessary side effects occurring.

Post-treatment care

Following each and every electrolysis treatment, the electrolgist should apply an aftercare product on cotton wool with both soothing and antiseptic effects. The properties found within aftercare products vary considerably, but may include the following:

✧ Witch hazel: a cooling gel or lotion which calms the skin, is mildly astringent and has antiseptic properties which promote the healing of skin tissues.
✧ Aloe vera: a natural product which is anti-bacterial and has calming and soothing properties.

Many other products have a diluted essential oil base such as:

✧ Tea tree: derived from a shrub or tree and is used for its anti-viral, anti-inflammatory, anti-biotic, and astringent properties, all of which promote the healing of the skin tissues and prevent the growth of bacteria.
✧ Lavender: derived from plant flowers and is used for its antiseptic, bactericidal, calming, and soothing properties, all of which help to heal wounds, sores and reduce the chance of bacterial infection occurring after electrolysis treatment.

There are a wide range of commercial products available, including tinted antiseptic creams which camourflage any redness. This allows clients to have treatment done during their lunch hour and return to work without embarrassment.

Some antiseptic preparations which contain anti-histamine are steroid-based creams and should be avoided as they are not recommended for use. They do not have the desired properties required for promoting skin tissue healing, as the others do. Betnovate will have an adverse effect, thinning the skin tissues after prolonged usage.

Post-treatment advice

During either the consultation or the first treatment the client should be informed of the normal skin reaction to electrolysis:

✧ Localised redness (erythema)
✧ Localised swelling within the tissues, around individual follicles
✧ Localised warmth within the tissues.

The client should also be informed that any reaction subsides very quickly lasting from 20 minutes to a few hours, rarely longer. The skin heals fairly promptly and there should be no visible sign of treatment having occurred on the skin's surface. Although occasionally there may be minute pinkish-brown scabs, when this occurs the scabs should drop off within a few days.

The above information should give the client confidence in both the electrolgist and the treatment and prevent any unnecessary worry. The aim of giving post-treatment care and advice is to:

✧ provide an antiseptic barrier to prevent infection occurring in the follicles
✧ to cool the skin as quickly as possible
✧ to promote healing of tissues.

The client should be advised to adhere closely to the post-treatment care advice to ensure that the tissues are allowed to heal promptly, preventing any adverse reaction occurring.

The following advice should be explained clearly.

✧ Avoid touching the area, to reduce the possibility of bacteria entering open follicles
✧ Apply recommended aftercare preparation for the next 24 hours, longer if the skin is slow to recover
✧ With the face area, avoid wearing face powder as this will block the open follicles and may lead to bacteria forming
✧ When cleansing skin, cleanse away from the area, to prevent bacteria entering the treatment area for 24 hours. Always recommend an appropriate cleanser for the skin type, for example milk for young combination skin, cream for normal to dry skin etc
✧ Avoid using any form of perfumed products such as soaps, shower gels, talcum powders or creams in the treatment area for 24 hours, again to prevent infection or irritation
✧ Do not wear make-up on the face or body for 24 hours following treatment, due to risk of clogging pores and formation of bacteria
✧ Sunbathing or the use of sunbeds is not recommended due to the risk of hyper-pigmentation in the treatment area
✧ Deep fat frying (cooking chips) is not recommended as hot fatty air rises and may lead to infected follicles and inflammation occurring
✧ If treating underarm area no deodorant is recommended for 24 hours, to prevent the risk of infection and irritation

✧ Generally no heat treatments of any type are recommended for 24 hours following electrolysis treatment due to the risk of irritation and inflammation
✧ Swimming in chlorinated water or salt may also irritate skin tissues
✧ Exercise after treatment may lead to perspiration salts entering open follicles and causing infection
✧ Tight clothing should be avoided in the area of treatment due to risk of irritation
✧ An antiseptic powder can be used to absorb moisture in areas such as axilla and bikini line.

Advice on how to manage hair growth in between treatments should be given as follows:
✧ Cut hairgrowth with nail scissors close to skin in-between treatments, but not within two days of having treatment.

The electrolgist should review every treatment with the client at the next visit to check skin reaction and healing, as adverse reactions can occur even with an experienced electrolgist, either due to the client's actions, medical conditions or a faulty technique.

Post-treatment problems

Bruising: discolouration of the skin tissues varying from black, blue, green to yellow in colouration. Appears immediately due to rupturing of blood vessels around the follicle. The main causes are:
✧ Poor technique, inaccurate probing, too deep into the tissues or incorrect angle, causes puncturing of the follicle wall.
✧ Too large a needle diameter forcing entry into follicle mouth.
✧ Clients who take aspirin or blood-thinning medication, for example warfarin, daily have a tendency to bruise more easily than others.

Generally, the skin heals quickly without any lasting effects. Apply cold compress to reduce discolouration.
✧ **Hypo-pigmentation:** this appears as lightening or white glassy patches of skin tissues. The main causes are:
✧ Coming out of the follicle with the current still on
✧ Cauterization of pigment cells in treatment area
✧ Probing too superficially
✧ Having the current intensity too high
✧ Probing follicles too closely together
✧ **Hyper-pigmentation:** is when the skin tissues darken, appearing as brown to purple patches on the skin, more common in darker skin types. The main causes are:
✧ Short wave diathermy current intensity too high

✧ Heat reaction causes the pigment cells to rise within the epidermis
✧ Probing follicles too close together.

This condition does not always fade. The electrologist should consider the following adaptations to treatment technique:
✧ Reduce treatment session time
✧ Space probes out 1 in 6 or 8 according to the area and skin and hair type
✧ Reduce current intensity
✧ Recommend the blend method
✧ Have longer gaps between treatments.

Permanent pitted scarring: this is when the surface of the epidermis is uneven with indentations which result in coarsening of the skin texture, causing a permanent change in the skin's structure. This should never occur.

The main causes are:
✧ Poor treatment technique, incorrect probing depth, too deep, thus damaging the germinative cells permanently so that any new cells are deformed
✧ Overtreating of an area leads to a build up of heat and cellular destruction
✧ Excessively high current intensity
✧ Constant picking of scabs can also cause pitting to occur
All of the above have long term permanent damage.
✧ **Temporary scarring/blanching of the tissues:** this appears as white raised rings on a red background, scabs form and drop off within a few days usually, leaving no long-term effects, if the client does not interfere with the treatment area.

The main causes are:
✧ Current intensity too high
✧ Probing too shallow
✧ Overtreating an area
✧ Leaving the current on when entering and leaving the follicle.
✧ **Honey coloured scabs:** this happens when tissue damage has occurred resulting in plasma seepage, usually heals within a few days with no long-term effects.

The main causes are:
✧ Current intensity too high
✧ Probing too shallow
✧ Poor insertion technique
✧ Treatment time too long.
✧ **Folliculitis:** this is a secondary infection which occurs as a result of bacteria entering the open follicle, bringing about inflammation and pus formation. The long-term effect is that of an indentation in the skin tissues, if the entire follicle is affected.
✧ **Orange peel effect:** the removal of coarse hairs from the top lip and chin may leave a

dimpled effect because coarse hairs grow from very wide follicles which sag when they close, once they are emptied, leaving small indentations on the skin's surface. Long-term, this effect fades.

✧ **Shrinkage of the tissues:** this usually occurs when a very close growth of coarse hairs are removed. As coarse hairs have large bulbs, when the hairs are removed and the follicles close there is a greater volume at the level of the bulb that at the level of the upper follicle. This causes a puckering effect on the surface of the skin. This effect on the skin will settle down and become smoother in time, depending on the elasticity of the skin.

✧ **Abnormal swelling:** this is the result of tissue irritation.

The main causes are:
✧ Overworking the area.
✧ Too long a treatment duration.
✧ Probing too close together.
✧ Current intensity too high.
✧ Apply a cold compress or ice pack to soothe tissues and reduce swelling.

✧ **Ingrowing hairs:** these are hairs which on emerging from the mouth of the hair follicle, either grow along under the skin's surface due to dead keratinised cells blocking the follicle mouth or turn back into the follicle opening becoming trapped. These hairs can cause irritation and become infected. Electro-epilation treatment cannot occur if there is infection present. The hair can be cut level with the skin and treated later once infection has gone. The hair can be freed from the skin using a micro-lance to allow it to rise up and be treated if not infected.

The main causes are:
✧ Dry skin
✧ Previous use of temporary hair removal methods, waxing and plucking
✧ Friction due to tight clothing
✧ Distorted hair follicles.

StudentActivity Tasks

Using the information you have acquired from this chapter and others, complete the following tasks.

✧ Design a professional quality post-treatment advice leaflet for clients

✧ Produce the above information on an A4 laminated display card for the reception area

✧ Design a professional leaflet on how electrolysis treatment works, is priced etc to be given to all prospective clients seeking general information on electrolysis treatment.

Advanced treatment techniques | 12

This chapter introduces you to a specialised area of diathermy using advanced techniques which some electrolgists may wish to progress to once they have acquired several years clinical experience, in order to offer additional treatments.

Whilst electrolysis is generally used for the removal of unwanted hairgrowth, it can also be used to treat a variety of vascular blemishes, by tapping into the capillaries, coagulating and cauterizing them. It is extremely successful at reducing facial capillaries, being very efficient and effective at a relatively low price when compared to laser therapy etc. Around 90 per cent – 95 per cent of treatments are generally successful, with only a small percentage of clients not responding to treatment for a variety of reasons, for example medication (contraceptive pill) or a recurring condition such as hayfever.

Leg thread veins do not respond as well as facial capillaries, they respond better to sclerotherapy, which is a chemical treatment which causes irritation to the lining of the blood vessels and leads to a clot forming and shrinkage of the vessels. Following treatment the area is bandaged.

Minor skin lesions such as warts and skin tags can also be treated successfully, however a higher insurance premium is charged and medical approval required.

Broken capillaries/Red veins/Thread veins (Telangiectasia): are the common terms used to describe a variety of blood vessels that are randomly dilated on an area of the face or body. Broken capillaries can be singular or multiple, varying in size and shape and occur more frequently in women than in men, giving a high/florid/red-bluish colour to the affected skin tissues. Northern Europeans with fair skin and dark hair are more prone to these conditions due to their skin being thin and fine in texture. Common sites for broken capillaries and spider naevi, are:

✧ Upper cheek areas and nasal area, with tissues being thinnest in these areas.
✧ Neck region.
✧ Leg areas.
✧ Although small singular blood spots do appear on the trunk more frequently with age.

Consultation

The consultation should be in-depth, establishing the following:

✧ Clients medical history.

✧ Medications being taken.

✧ Any contra-indications.

✧ Whether the skins healing rate is good, average, poor.

✧ If there is a tendency to bruise easily; this should be noted as there may be a congenital weakness of the capillaries.

✧ The clients occupation should be identified, this may be a contributing factor.

✧ Type of diet regularly eaten, for example bland, spicy, rich etc, alcohol units consumed per week, amount of tea or coffee drank daily, any other stimulants taken regularly.

✧ Whether the client is a smoker/non-smoker, as this affects the skins breathing.

All of the above will help to identify a probable cause of telangiectasia, and may have an effect on the outcome of the treatment etc.

The treatment procedure should be discussed with the client and a test patch carried out to establish how the skin responds to treatment and its healing rate. This will enable the electrologist to determine the frequency of treatment, length of treatment time and if extensive treatment is required.

Contra-indications to treatment

During the consultation contra-indications should be checked for, as some contra-indications only restrict treatment whilst others require medical approval or prevent treatment from being given. The following should be checked for:

Haemophilia: prevents treatment as there is a problem with blood being able to clot.

Hepatitis B: is contra-indicated as it is a highly infectious viral condition which takes a long time to recover from fully. Once the virus has gone the client will require written consent from their GP to state that treatment can now go ahead.

Aids: (Acquired immunodeficiency syndrome): is contra-indicated as this is a viral infection which poses a high risk of cross infection to the electrolgist due to the fact that the virus is easily transmitted via body fluids. The HIV virus which eventually leads to Aids does not survive long outside the body and is less infectious, so is thought to pose less risk of cross infection. If in doubt always seek medical advice.

Medication: some medicines taken regularly affect the blood's clotting mechanism, for example warfarin and aspirin are anti-coagulants and increase the likelihood of the blood vessels leaking following treatment. Some antibiotics can cause spider naevi to form.

Epilepsy: requires medical approval for the same reasons as stated with epilation, treatment of telangiectasia is precision work and the risk of client 'fitting' is not conducive to this work.

Keloid scarring: clients who suffer from this condition should not be treated due to the risk of scarring occurring wherever treatment is carried out.

Diabetes: this condition generally means that the skin has a poor healing response, clients tend to have poor sensory nerve response, and lower pain thresholds. Treatment can be carried out in some cases with GP approval and guidance.

Allergies: anyone who is allergic to the type of metal that needles are made from, this will prohibit treatment being carried out.

Asthma, hay fever and sinus sufferers: clients suffering with any of the above conditions often have broken capillaries around the nostrils, this is due to narrowing of the air passages, resulting in reduced oxygen supply to the skin tissues and pressure on the nostrils from sneezing or continual blowing of the nose. Treatment is not very successful long-term due to the condition recurring.

Nervous clients: clients of a nervous disposition should be advised against this treatment due to the risk of scarring, as they are less likely to relax and are more prone to being 'jumpy' and likely to pull away during treatment.

Tight clothing: the wearing of constricting clothing such as hold-up stockings and pop socks etc, can cause a restriction in the blood flow and result in broken capillaries or thread veins on the legs, and would prohibit treatment being given if practice were to continue.

Skin diseases or infections: are contra-indicated for obvious reasons. (Revisit chapter 4)

Varicose veins: these can not be treated by the electrolgist, neither can large blue, or green veins.

Fine thin fragile skin: is too delicate to treat as it suffers from poor circulation. Remember if presented with a condition that you lack knowledge of do not be persuaded to treat; always seek medical advice.

Causes of Telangiectasia

When this condition occurs it is because the tiny blood capillaries which feed the dermis become permanently dilated and rupture, rising up within the layers of the skin, where they become trapped, showing through the epidermis, giving a pink or bluish tinge to the skin. There are many factors which can cause this condition to result for example:

Hereditary: if you are born with a congenital weakness of the capillaries, you are more likely to develop this condition.

Trauma to the skin tissues: any heavy blow, pressure or squeezing of the tissues, for example (wearing of spectacles, picking spots, squeezing blackheads) may cause permanent dilation of capillaries.

Age: as we age, our skin tissues thin, both the skin and blood vessels lose elasticity, and any dilated capillaries become more pronounced. This happens more so in the upper cheek and nasal areas of the face as the tissues are particularly thin and delicate in this area.

Medications: some medications can bring about this condition, for example steroid creams applied regularly for a prolonged period have the effect of thinning the skin tissues, Retin-A; an acne treatment preparation, this also has an adverse effect on the capillaries long-term.

Ultraviolet radiation: excessive exposure to natural or artificial sunlight leads to skin damage, with UVA rays penetrating the dermis and causing damage to the collagen and elastin fibres which leads to premature ageing of the tissues, dehydration and a tendency for telangiectasia to form. Always recommend clients use an ultraviolet radiation protection cream.

Medical conditions: high blood pressure, causes dilated capillaries due to the high pressure in the vessels. Liver disease tends to lead to broken capillaries. Diabetic skins have a tendency to bruise more readily due to slow coagulation of the blood, and therefore are prone to telangiectasia. Asthmatics also have a tendency to suffer with broken facial capillaries due to the narrowing of the airways which brings about a reduction in the oxygen supply to the skin tissues, giving a reddish/blue tinge to the skin tissues.

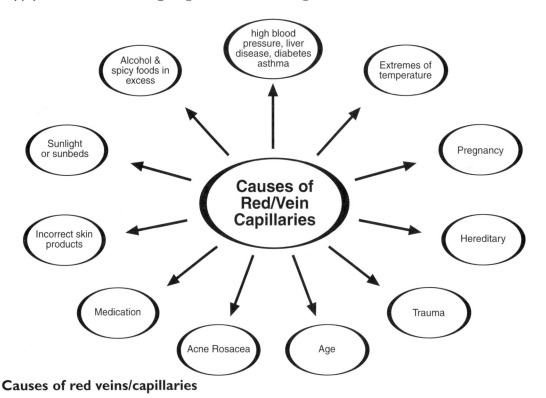

Causes of red veins/capillaries

Hormones: pregnancy often leads to the formation of facial telangiectasia due to raised hormone levels, and increased blood flow, these sometimes disappear after child birth, however if treated with electrolysis they respond well.

Temperature extremes: people who work outdoors in extremes of temperature, for example farmers, gardeners etc, are prone to having very weathered skin with reddish blue tinges where broken capillaries have formed. The function of blood vessels is to help regulate body temperature as the environment changes, for example when we get hot the capillaries dilate, rising to the skin surface, giving a flushed appearance and helping to cool the body temperature. In cold weather the vessels constrict keeping the blood deep within the body, leaving the skin pale in colour. With exposure to extremes of temperature the vessels become permanently dilated. Also, washing your face in hot water followed by cold water is damaging to the capillaries, always use tepid water.

Diet: excessive drinking of alcohol, hot drinks or eating hot spicy foods brings about dilation of the blood capillaries which over a period of time leads to the formation of telangiectasia.

Skin products: incorrect product types, for example using products which are too strong for skin type, or excessive use of exfoliating products can cause an abrasive action. This strips the skin surface and stimulates a vascular response, initiating dehydration, and leading to permanent dilation of the capillaries in the face.

Acne rosacea: occurs after 30 years of age. With this skin condition there is permanent dilation of the skin tissues across the upper cheeks and nose. It is usually quite severe and requires medical treatment as it becomes progressively worse with age.

Treatment Procedure For Red Veins/Capillaries

The aim of electrolysis when treating dilated, ruptured capillaries, is to block the flow of the blood by cauterizing and coagulating it, forming a small clot or bruise which prevents the blood flowing to the skin surface. Once capillaries have been treated, new normal size capillaries will regrow, and find another route to efficiently nourish the skin tissues without showing through the skin's surface.

Procedure

✧ The electrologist should wash his/her hands with anti-bactericidal cleanser and applies latex gloves.
✧ Cleanse the skin tissues with a milk cleanser and tone.
✧ Wipe over the skin with an antiseptic solution, for example medi-swab which is alcohol based.
✧ Check test patch to see the skin's healing response.
✧ Select a short fine sharp and sterile needle, use either a Sterex gold 003 or a Ballet F2.
✧ Identify the feeder capillary/vein by very gently stroking the treatment area with the skin tissues held taut. This enables you to identify from which direction the capillary is filling. (If the capillary does not drain do not treat).
✧ Insert the sterile needle very gently and not very deeply into the red vein/capillary working from the furthermost point towards the most prominent part of the capillary.

◇ Apply the current along the length of the capillary in a tapping technique, for a minimum amount of time, keeping the current below the skin surface and leaving gaps between insertions.

The immediate effect once the current is released is one of blanching/whitening of the skin tissues and the blood appears to vanish instantly as the current seals the blood vessel. There is also a mild erythema and mild localised swelling, a normal heat reaction. Treatment continues until the area is treated or until skin starts to become noticeably red. The first treatment should always be kept short, 5 minutes maximum according to the skin's response, then subsequent treatment times may be increased if appropriate.

1. Techniques for red veins
Stretch skin gently
Probe needle slowly and gently into the skin tissues
discharge current to seal blood vessels

2. Spider Naeus
Treatment procedure select prominent blood vessels and tap into it at intervals to seal off blood vessels.

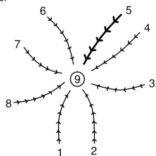

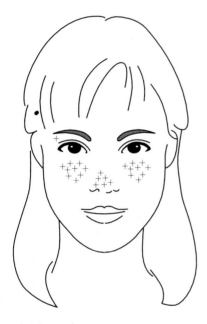

Facial locations

The electrologist should arrange to see the client approximately 3 to 4 weeks later, to see how the skin has responded to treatment and to allow the area to fully heal. Subsequent treatments can only be carried out once the skin has fully healed.

If treatment is extensive and involves several areas of the face then regular biweekly appointments can be arranged with the electrologist working on different areas, staggering treatment and allowing each area to fully heal before retreating it. A well documented record card must be kept to know which area was treated at each visit and to plot overall progress. Taking a photograph at the start of extensive treatment is a good way of demonstrating how effective treatment has been.

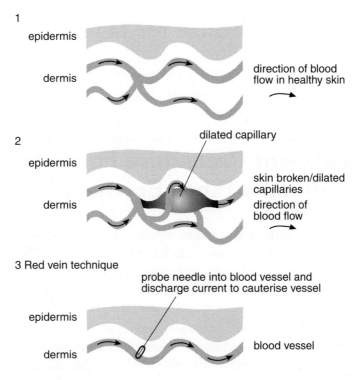

1

epidermis

dermis

direction of blood
flow in healthy skin

2

dilated capillary

epidermis

dermis

skin broken/dilated
capillaries

direction of
blood flow

3 Red vein technique

probe needle into blood vessel and
discharge current to cauterise vessel

epidermis

dermis

blood vessel

A cross section of skin tissues

Treatment Procedure For Spider Naevi

A spider naevus is a collection of fine dilated capillaries which radiate out from a centrally dilated blood vessel resembling a spider. This is common to the face but may arise anywhere on the body. Generally spider naevus respond well to treatment.

The treatment technique is similar to red veins/capillaries: insert a sterile, sharp needle into the capillaries radiating out, for example the 'legs', tapping along the length and working towards the centrally dilated blood spot. When 'all legs' have been treated you can treat the central vessel from where the blood flows. The skin reaction is the same as with red veins/capillaries, mild erythema, localised swelling and blanching of the tissues. The current intensity is minimal and held on for a fraction of time to prevent burning of the tissues resulting. If there are multiple spider naevi then you would have to stagger treatment as with red veins/capillaries.

Treatment Procedure for Dot Telangiectasia

These are small red blood spots, which should only be treated if bright red and nearly level with the skin's surface. This procedure requires probing to be a little deeper into the centre of the dilated vessel than with red veins/capillaries.

Treatment Procedure For Skin Tags (Papillomas/Fibro Epithelial Polyps)

Skin tags are fibrous growths of skin tissue, which may be raised on stalks (penduculated) or flat, varying in colour from pale pink to dark brown. Size and shape also varies considerably. Common sites are neck and axilla areas, may be singular or multiple.

◇ The electrologist should wash hands with anti-bactericidal skin cleanser and applies latex gloves

◇ Cleanse the skin tissue with a skin cleanser and tone

◇ Wipe treatment area with an antiseptic solution, for example a medi-swab

◇ Select a strong fine sterile needle according to size of skin tag to be treated, for example 005, 006, 010

◇ If treating a large skin tag a higher current intensity will be required. If treating a small to medium size skin tag select a medium current intensity

◇ With sterile tweezers hold the skin tag lifting it away from the skin tissues and either insert the needle into the stalk or around the outer borders of skin tag according to type, and discharge the current to cauterize the area

◇ Observe the surrounding skin tissues for any sign of heat reaction and modify accordingly.

The treatment does not always produce an instant result with skin tags coming away immediately. The skin tag often goes darker in colour and drops off a few days to a week later.

The electrologist completes treatment by applying an antiseptic pad, usually witch hazel based. Advice for client with regard to post-treatment care of area is similar to advice given for dilated capillaries.

After Care

As this treatment is an invasive one, attention to hygiene must be a priority for both the electrologist and the client, to ensure that no bacteria enters the open treatment area and results in an adverse skin reaction.

Therefore on completion of the treatment the electrologist applies a cool damp antiseptic pad to the area to help the healing process, which may include any one of the following products:

✧ Witch hazel gel
✧ Essential oil of Lavender
✧ Tee tree oil or lotion
✧ Lacto-calamine
✧ Caladryl
✧ Sterex apre's lotion.

Within a few days' time, minute scabs usually form. These should be left whilst the tissues heal as they protect the area from bacteria. The scabs will drop off given time and should not be helped to drop off or scarring will result.

Homecare Advice

The following advice should always be given following any form of red vein/capillary work to the client:

✧ Apply recommended after care product on a damp cotton wool pad for 24 to 48 hours until small scabs have appeared and sealed skin tissues from bacteria.
✧ Do not wear make-up for 48 hours.
✧ Avoid touching or stretching the skin for 48 hours.
✧ Do not wash the treatment area for 24 hours.
✧ Avoid hot steamy atmospheres, for example sauna, steam rooms.
✧ Do not exercise or sunbathe for 48 hours, this increases blood flow in the treatment area.
✧ Avoid using any perfumed products in the treatment area for 48 hours, for example soaps, creams, perfumes etc.
✧ If a body area is covered, avoid wearing tight clothing.
✧ Remind the client that treatment involved cauterization of blood vessels which produces a minor internal burn which should be treated with extra care and protection for 48 hours.
✧ The skin will heal normally and leave no adverse reaction if the client follows advice correctly.
✧ Tell the client when to return for re-assessment and further treatment if appropriate.
✧ Also advise client to ring you if they have any concerns regarding treatment etc.

review**questions**

Q1 Define the term advanced electrolysis.

Q2 State what is the correct term used to describe red veins/capillaries.

Q3 List six common causes of red veins/capillaries.

Q4 Name six contra-indications to red veins/capillaries treatment.

Q5 State how the red veins/capillaries treatment procedure differs from normal electrolysis hair removal treatment.

Q6 Define the term skin tag.

Q7 State what size needles are more suitable for treating skin tags.

Q8 List two common sites for red veins/capillaries to be located on the body.

Q9 Name two common sites for skin tags to grow.

Q10 Name the type of insurance required to carry out red veins/capillaries treatment.

Q11 List three pieces of post-treatment advice to be given to the client following red veins treatment.

Q12 State two reasons for staggering treatments when dealing with an extensive areas of red veins.

Gender reassignment | 13

This chapter aims to give a brief overview on gender reassignment, to enable the electrologist to have an understanding of the main reason behind why individuals seek this option. It also gives an insight into the treatment of transsexuals with a treatment plan outline.

Male to female gender reassignment

A transsexual is any individual who has been born biologically either a man or a women who psychologically feels trapped within the wrong gender body and desperately wishes to change gender. They are prepared to undergo both major surgery to change their gender, which is known as gender reassignment, and detailed psychological analysis by a psychiatrist specialising in gender dysphoria.

This is by no means an easy option for an individual, they have usually struggled, emotionally with their beliefs for years, sometimes even decades, trying to ignore these feelings and pursue what is known as a 'normal life', marriage, family and a career, only to have to walk away when they can no longer ignore their feelings, which become progressively stronger with time. The process of gender reassignment is a lengthy one and requires major upheavals in their life and career. Lifelong relationships are often destroyed, once this process starts. The transsexual has to break through several medical, social, physical and emotional barriers prior to being recommended for gender reassignment surgery. They have to go through lengthy psychological analysis, to ensure that they genuinely want and need this treatment, and are psychologically able to cope with all that it entails. During this period the transsexual will have to work and live as either a women or man according to the gender type they wish to change to for a period of one- to two-year period, before they can be referred for surgery. They have to establish a group of social relationships with both sexes and be emotionally stable, undergo hormonal therapy and electro-epilation if beard removal is required prior to receiving surgery for gender reassignment.

Male to female gender reassignment

This is the most common form of gender reassignment. During the period of psychological assessment prior to surgery, the transsexual has to undertake a high dosage hormone therapy programme, for the physiological and physical changes to their body to occur, creating the outwards appearance of a female. This involves taking feminising hormones, oestrogen and progesterone to develop female secondary sexual characteristics. Also an androgen suppressant may be prescribed, to reduce the effect of the male sex hormones being produced within the transexual's body. (Oestrogen itself suppresses androgens to a degree, but a supplement is required by some individuals to suppress androgen levels sufficiently for the physiological process of change to occur successfully).

The changes the transsexual experiences as a result of hormone therapy to a degree mimic puberty in the female. They will experience similar emotional problems adjusting to the physiological changes they experience, for example:

◇ there is the development of breast buds, pigmentation and enlargement of the areolar and eventually fully developed breasts

◇ the body shape changes, due to redistribution, as oestrogen lays down fat cells, which give females their curves, waist and hips. Women have a higher body fat percentage than men

◇ emotions may be heightened, resulting in mood swings, depression, anxiety or nervousness

◇ oestrogen hormones reduce the sebaceous gland activity and improve the general skin's appearance, smoother, softer, finer textured than a male's generally

◇ there is an improvement in hair texture on the scalp and a softening of beard hairgrowth.

The other physiological changes that occur at this stage due to hormone therapy may include:

◇ the testes shrink in size

◇ impotence

◇ sterility.

Hormone therapy will not affect the beard growth, it will still require extensive electro-epilation or some form of laser therapy, for longterm hair removal to result and improve physical appearance inducing a feminine facial appearance. Treatment for beard growth can range from 2–4 years with twice weekly treatments of between 1 and 2 hours depending on hairgrowth, density, strength, etc. If body hairgrowth is dense, further treatment will be required. This treatment process is rarely available on the National Health and is a huge financial commitment for the transsexual, ideally it should commence at the start of the 2-year period of living as a female prior to surgery and continue for sometime after surgery. See the treatment plan outlined on page 172.

Hormone therapy also does not alter the masculine voice, speech therapy will be required to alter pitch etc. If the transsexual has any form of baldness, hormone therapy will not stimulate scalp hairgrowth, and either a good quality hairpiece will need to be purchased or a hair transplant considered. Hair transplant can be a lengthy process as well as a financial commitment.

Once the physiological changes have occurred there may be a need for any minor cosmetic surgery such as rhinoblast-nose reduction, or breast augmentation (breast enlargement), this will also involve a financial cost to the transsexual, as it may not be possible to get this treatment under the National Health.

The surgery involved in gender reassignment includes:
✧ the removal of the testes
✧ building of a pseudo-vagina
✧ breast augmentation.

The transexual may be given help or lessons on application of make-up, glamour or camouflage, advice on general good grooming, for example how to walk, and look after hands, nails etc, through the hospital they are under.

Treatment plan for transsexual beard removal

Treatment of transsexuals is an extensive programme and the client will need to continue shaving initially throughout the treatment process for several reasons:
✧ psychologically, they are trying to become feminine and hairgrowth or beard shadow is demoralising and depressing.
✧ they have to live, work and be accepted socially as a female, which is difficult to achieve if you have a full beard or a 5 o'clock shadow.

The preferred method of electro-epilation is the blend for the following reasons:
✧ its ability to treat distorted follicles and coarse hairgrowth with less regrowth resulting.
✧ short wave diathermy has an increased risk of hyper-pigmentation as the client is undertaking high dosage hormone therapy and also has a higher degree of regrowth, which will be demoralising for the client.

The general aim of this type of treatment programme initially is to concentrate on improving the hair texture, fining and thinning it out and to reduce the colour tone of the beard shadow.

When undertaking this type of extensive treatment programme you need to divide the beard growth up into treatment areas and work in a checker board fashion, treating one area of hairgrowth during one of the weekly sessions and use the second weekly session for any regrowth hairs. Commence treatment at the sideburn areas below ear level, gradually working inwards and downwards over cheek areas, then treating chin, upper lip, before working down jaw line towards neck, eventually treating the sternum area. The coarse nature of the hairgrowth may require high levels of galvanic current. Generally, the skin tissues respond well to this treatment, however it is always advisable to complete the treatment with cataphoresis which will balance the skins tissues, neutralising the effects of the chemical sodium hydroxide.

Transexual clients often prefer to have evening appointments, to avoid meeting other clients and to be able to confide and discuss their problems with the electrologist, until they are comfortable and confident with their own body and general appearance.

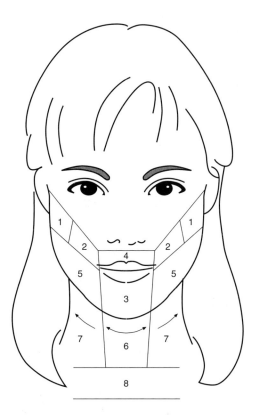

Treatment plan

Gender reassignment female to male

These are transsexuals who are biologically female who wish to be male. This is rarer but also involves lengthy psychological analysis, hormone therapy and surgery. This form of gender reassignment does not usually require the services of an electrologist, as the transsexual is wanting to increase facial and body hairgrowth and not its removal.

There is a long period of psychological assessment with this form of gender reassignment also; the transexual has to undertake a high dosage hormone therapy programme, for the physiological and physical changes to their body to occur, creating the outwards appearance of male. This involves taking the male hormone testosterone.

The changes the transsexual experiences as a result of hormone therapy to a degree mimic puberty in the male. They will experience similar emotional problems adjusting to the physiological changes they experience, for example:

✧ the deepening of the voice to form a masculine voice, usually within a few months of starting hcrmone treatment
✧ mood swings, and possible aggression
✧ cessation of menstruation within 6 months on average
✧ acne may result due to high levels of the hormone testosterone
✧ the development of muscular bulk, weight and increased strength
✧ redistribution of body fat, males have a lower body fat percentage than females
✧ the breasts shrink
✧ increased general body hairgrowth and the development of a beard
✧ permanent clitoral enlargement
✧ coarsening of the skin's texture.

Other changes include:
✧ sterility.

Several operations will be required and include:
✧ a full hysterectomy and oophorectomy to remove the ovaries and womb
✧ the removal of the breasts, (mastectomy)
✧ the construction of a micro-pseudo phallus like structure
✧ scrotoplasty surgery may be to create a scrotum, from the labia and silicone implants.

Generally within 18 months to 2 years the female's appearance has change beyond recognition and is wholly male.

The following is an outline of a possible transsexual treatment plan.

Age: 42 years.
Sex: Transexual male-gender choice female
Nationality: British.
Medical condition: None noted.
Occupation: Graphics designer
Treatment area: Beard
Probable cause: Normal male pattern

Hair Type: Dense dark thick coarse hairgrowth on chin, sides of face, neck and top lip.
Skin type: Dry and dehydrated.
Treatment method: The blend.
Needle size 005

Twice weekly treatment of 1 hour duration, first session and to treat new area, second session to clear regrowth as treatment progresses. This treatment format would generally take about 18 months.

Treatment would continue weekly for possibly another year at weekly 1 hour sessions depending on progress made. Then reduce to 6 months of fortnightly 1 hour sessions, followed by 6 months of monthly 1 hour sessions and then treatment as required to tidy up regrowth. However, treatment progress is dependant on the client's commitment to regular treatment and the original density of hairgrowth and experience of the electrologist.

review**questions**

Q1 Define the term transsexual.

Q2 Name three processes a transsexual has to go through prior to having surgery.

Q3 Name two hormones involved in male to female gender reassignment.

Q4 Identify two types of surgery which may occur with male to female reassignment.

Q5 Which method of electro-epilation is likely to be more effective when treating coarse beard growth? Explain your answer.

Q6 When undertaking extensive beard work, what format should hair removal take?

Q7 List four physical changes that occur when on high dosage oestrogen hormone therapy.

Q8 With female to male gender reassignment, what role does the electrologist play?

Q9 With an extensive treatment programme is it possible to predict the length of time treatment will take?

Q10 Name four factors that need to be considered by the electrologist when treating a transsexual.

Q11 The progress of a treatment is always discussed with the client when treating a transsexual. Who else should be kept informed of treatment progress?

Q12 Explain why long-term psychological analysis is necessary for all transsexual clients.

Case studies

14

This chapter looks at a selection of case studies to show how treatment plans are formulated and adapted, leading to successful treatment results, based on information gained both during the consultation from the client, as well as from the electrologist's experience when treating the client's hairgrowth problem, with either electrolysis or intense pulsed light therapy. It also gives an insight into the treatment of transsexuals with a treatment plan outline. The case studies included in this chapter have either been treated by the authors Glynis Turpin and Hilary Cowley, who have given permission for their work to be included within this chapter.

Client Profile No 1

Age:	38 years.
Sex:	Female.
Nationality:	British.
Medical Condition:	None noted.
Occupation:	Nurse.
Treatment area:	Top lip, chin, sides of face and neck.
Probable cause:	Hormonal and topical stimulation. Dark fine hairgrowth occurred around the time of pregnancy, initially client plucked hairgrowth daily, but as it increased she resorted to shaving eventually having to shave twice a day morning and night due to a 5 o'clock shadow. Eleven years previously she had sought electrolysis treatment but was under the impression that she only needed 1 or 2 treatments to alleviate the problem, so gave up thinking electrolysis did not work and went back to shaving. Client extremely embarrassed by hairgrowth, introverted and did not socialise much, spoke with her hand over her mouth and worn high necked clothing to conceal hairgrowth at neck. Her husband contacted me first, and I explained that I could help his wife but it would need to be her decision to contact and seek treatment with me, which she did some months later after getting to know me socially.

Hair Type: Dark thick coarse hairgrowth of chin sides of face, neck and top lip.
Skin type: Dry and dehydrated.

Treatment method: Short wave diathermy, 40 minutes twice weekly for 6 months, then weekly, concentrating initially on the most prominent area the chin and sides of face. As hair growth reduced and was under control we commenced work on the neck area, treating any regrowth areas at the same time. Once the neck area was under control we were able to treat all areas of face for regrowth in a 20–30 minute session, eventually starting on and concentrating on treating top lip area. Working across the top lip thinning hairgrowth out, until again hairgrowth reduced and treatment became spasmodic awaiting any regrowth to come through and having a tidy-up session as required. The complete treatment took 3 years. The client was extremely committed, always following home care advice and by the end of the course she had developed her self confidence and was no longer frightened to socialise, being far more outgoing, wore facial make-up and no longer talked covering her face with her hands.

Client Profile No 2

Age: 14 years.
Sex: Female.
Nationality: British.
Medical Condition: Hormonal imbalance.
Occupation: School girl.
Treatment area: Top lip and chin.
Probable cause: Hormonal.

The client came with her mother for a consultation, both were very embarrassed and highly emotional regarding the hairgrowth problem. They had previously sought medical advice from an unsympathetic GP who's assessment was negative and advice unhelpful.

The hairgrowth was abnormal in an adolescent being excessive terminal hairgrowth on the top lip and chin areas. The client had never tampered with hairgrowth.

The electrologist suggested that the client see an endocrinologist, explaining that they would need a GP referral to do this, subsequently the client changed GP to a more sympathetic one.

Sometime later the client returned, having seen an endocrinologist, who had put her on a high dose progesterone pill to stabilise the hormone imbalance, he also suggested she return to have electrolysis treatment to reduce the hairgrowth problem.

Hair Type: Excessive coarse dark terminal hair.
Skin type: Combination skin with an oily T panel and normal cheeks no blemishes.

Treatment method: Short wave diathermy for 30 minutes every week for 4 weeks. Treatment then reduced to 15 minute sessions every fortnight for 6 months. Treatment areas responded very fast, with a very small percentage of regrowth, probably due to the medication prescribed. The client and her mother were extremely pleased with the success of the treatment.

The real cause of the hairgrowth problem remained unknown: a hormonal imbalance was the only medical information given.

Client Profile No 3

Age:	58 years.
Sex:	Female.
Nationality:	British.
Medical Condition:	None noted.
Occupation:	Admin officer.
Treatment area:	Top lip and chin.
Probable cause:	Hormonal and topical stimulation.

The client first noticed fine dark odd hairs appearing at approximately 50 years of age on the chin, with fine hairgrowth on the top lip probably as a result of a hormonal imbalance due to menopause. Client had regularly plucked hairgrowth on chin until problem became too widespread to deal with, but had never tampered with top lip. She then decided to try electrolysis after being recommended by a friend to the clinic.

Hair type:	Closely compacted fine textured hair on top lip. Whilst chin area had dark thick coarse terminal hairgrowth on either side of the chin.
Skin type:	Dry with a mild sensitivity to products, skin generally has good healing ability.

Treatment method: short wave diathermy weekly for 20 minute sessions for 4 weeks to clear areas, concentrating on chin areas whilst thinning top lip as time permitted.

Skin reaction normal, applied witch hazel gel to area as client knew this product suited her skin type.

Treatment then progressed to fortnightly 20 minute sessions for 3 months treating both chin and top lip, regrowth on top lip minimal with chin hairs finer and more spaced out. Treatment then given at monthly intervals for 6 months. The client was very pleased with the success of treatment, but understood that she may need spasmodic treatments to tidy up any odd regrowth hairs, which were likely to occur due to the nature of the problem. It was left that she booked a 10 minute tidy-up session 6 months later, but should ring if treatment required sooner. The client then had 3 further 6 monthly tidy-up sessions.

Client Profile No 4

Age:	27 years.
Sex:	Male.
Nationality:	British.
Medical condition:	None noted.
Occupation:	Male model and actor.
Treatment area:	Between the eyebrows and on top of the nose.
Probable cause:	Normal hairgrowth.

The eyebrows did however meet in the middle resembling one large brow and there were a few isolated hairs on the nose. The client was concerned by the isolated hairs on his nose and the hairgrowth between brows, wishing it cleared to leave two brows, due to the nature of his work the isolated hairs on the nose showed up when photographed like tree trunks in his words, and female friends joked about his one eyebrow, his agent had recommended he seek electrolysis to alleviate the problem. The client had never had any form of hair removal before.

Hair type:	Coarse thick dark hairgrowth in eyebrow region. Fine textured dark brown hair on nose.
Skin type:	Normal

Treatment method: short wave diathermy 2 weekly sessions of 20 minutes, this treated both areas, hairgrowth on nose very shallow epilated easily, brow hair shallow but strong root attachment requiring a higher current intensity than other area. These treatments were followed by 2 sessions of fortnightly treatment concentrating on brow area for 15 minutes. Then 1 month later a 10 minute treatment session removing all remaining regrowth hairs.

Client was advised to return in the event of any further regrowth occurring at a later date. He was extremely pleased with the finished result of the eyebrows and showed me modelling photographs of himself before and after treatment.

Client Profile No 5

Age:	28 years.
Sex:	Female.

Nationality: British.
Medical condition: None noted.
Occupation: Class room assistant.
Treatment area: Lower legs.
Probable cause: Puberty and topical stimulation.

The client had shaved her legs since early teens daily from ankle to hip, then switched to regular waxing treatments since early twenties. The client was a very tall leggy attractive young lady who was extremely embarrassed and self-conscious about the hairgrowth, to the extent of wearing 2 pairs of dark tights when wearing skirts, but generally living in trousers to conceal hairgrowth. The plan was to alleviate the hairgrowth from ankle to knee to allow client to be able to wear short skirts and shorts during summer months. Client was well aware on the commitment required for a course of extensive treatment and was fully committed.

Hair type: Thick dark terminal hairgrowth.
Skin type: Normal to dry, small scars around ankle areas from shaving.

Treatment method: short-wave diathermy. Weekly treatments of l hour duration concentrating on the left leg first, hairs epilated well, generally. Fourth treatment commenced on the right leg for l hour. Once both legs had been cleared once, treatment 8 and successive treatments alternated between legs reducing regrowth. Hairgrowth responded well to treatment, better than initially expected, probably due to the client having previously waxed the majority of hairgrowth in the growing phase at start of treatment. Also whilst the hair was thick and dark, follicles were well spaced and treatment progressed quickly. At the end of 6 months the lower legs were both clear to the knee level. Client was thrilled and commenced treatment on upper thigh area. Several years later this client is still hair free, and a great ambassador for electrolysis treatment.

Client Profile No 6

Age: 30 years.
Sex: Female.
Nationality: Caribbean.
Medical condition: Poly cystic ovaries and duodenal ulcers.
Occupation: Foster Carer.
Treatment area: Chin.
Probable cause: Hormonal.

Hair problem appeared after an operation for duodenal ulcers at the age of 21 years. The client was also diagnosed with polycystic ovaries syndrome. She had previously had short wave diathermy treatment for a period of 7 years, with only a slight improvement prior to seeking treatment from me.

Hair type: Thick, dark, curly, coarse, deep terminal hairgrowth.

Skin type: Afro-Caribbean, dark moist skin. Chin area had lumps from plucking and hyper-pigmentation in the area, probably from previous treatment method.

Treatment method: the blend. Carried out a test patch on a few hairs using an insulated steel needle and the blend, with settings on 28 HF and .4 DC. The hairs were very strong. The skin healed well, with no hyper-pigmentation or keloid scarring resulting. Treatment plan started with 4 weekly sessions of 15 minutes duration with settings on 28 HF and .5 DC. This was followed by 7 fortnightly treatments of 15 minutes duration, using 28 HF and .5–6 DC. Treatments then changed to 12, four-weekly sessions still of 15 minute duration, with settings changing to 28 HF and .5–7 DC. The client was thrilled to see the results, fewer hairs on chin area and hairgrowth much finer.

Treatments then changed to 3, three-monthly treatments, on the same settings. The last treatment session was 10 weeks ago, with regrowth finer, sparse and skin settled with no adverse reactions resulting from treatments given.

Client No 7

Age: 39 years.

Sex: Female.

Nationality: Caribbean.

Medical condition: None noted.

Occupation: Health visitor.

Treatment area: Chin and cheeks.

Probable cause: Hereditary and topical stimulation. The client had plucked hairgrowth daily.

Hair type: Thick, dark, curly, coarse, deep terminal hairgrowth.

Skin type: Afro-Caribbean, dark moist skin. Prone to hyper-pigmentation at trauma sites, for example spots or insect bites.

Treatment method: the blend. Carried out a test patch on 6 hairs, to check for keloid reaction, using an insulated steel needle 004 size. Good response, skin healed normally. Hairs very, very strong. Treatment plan started with 4 weekly sessions of 15 minutes duration, treating chin and cheeks, with settings on 28 HF and .6 DC. This was followed by 5 fortnightly treatments of 20 minutes duration using 28 HF and .6–8 DC. Treatments then changed to 4, three-weekly treatments of 20 minutes duration, treating each area.

Both the client and myself were very pleased with results at this stage, as hairgrowth had noticeably thinned and become finer in texture. There were no problems with the skin healing or any adverse reactions.

Treatments then changed to 2 once-monthly sessions with settings on 28 HF and .6 DC followed by, 7 six-weekly treatment sessions with settings on 28 HF and .5 DC. 6 followed by two monthly treatments of 15 minutes duration on settings of 28 HF and .5–6 DC.

The client has since had 4 treatments which range between 3 and 5 monthly intervals for 15 minutes duration to tidy all areas. The needle size has been reduced 003, whilst settings remained the same for HF and DC.

Client Profile No 8

Age: 17 years.
Sex: Female.
Nationality: British.
Medical condition: None noted.
Occupation: Student.
Treatment area: Around navel and upper abdomen.
Probable cause: Possibly hereditary and topical. Client hairgrowth occurred at puberty and client had previously plucked and shaved areas, before seeking intense pulsed light treatment.
Hair type: Dark brown coarse thick deep terminal hair.
Skin type: II, always burns and sometimes tans.
Treatment method: Intense pulsed light therapy.
Time: 15 minutes.

Treatment plan:	Test patch	Treatment 1	Treatment 2
Fluence	36	36	36
Filter	615	615	615
Pulses	2	2	2
Duration	5	5	5
Delay	20	20	15

The client had a test patch and two treatments of 30 minutes, then treatment 3 used the same settings as treatment 2, but took only 15 minutes. Treatments were 8 weeks apart.

Changes to settings were made as hairs regrew finer.

Client Profile No 9

Age: 35 years.
Sex: Female.

Nationality: British.
Medical condition: Polycystic Ovary Syndrome.
Occupation: Housewife formerly nurse.
Treatment area: Neck, chin and top lip.
Probable cause: Polycystic Ovary Syndrome and topical stimulation.

Client's hairgrowth occurred after pregnancy, the client had 3 children under the age of 4 years of age, and had treated hairgrowth with a variety of temporary methods of hair removal, before seeking intense pulsed light therapy.

Hair type: Dark brown coarse deep terminal hair.
Skin type: II always burns and sometimes tans.
Treatment method: Intense pulsed light therapy.
Time: 30 minutes.

Treatment plan:	Test patch	Treatment 1	Treatment 2
Fluence	36	38	38
Filter	615	615	615
Pulses	2	2	2
Duration	4.2	4.2	4.2
Delay	15	15	15

Treatment interval was 8 weeks between treatments and is still on-going at time of writting this book.

Client Profile No 10

Age: 25 years.
Sex: Female.
Nationality: Mediterranean origin.
Medical condition: None noted.
Occupation: Sales manager and aerobics instructor.
Treatment area: Abdomen and bikini line.
Probable cause: Racial/hereditary.

Client's hairgrowth occurred around puberty, and she had previously treated hairgrowth through shaving initally and then electrolysis, but wanted a quicker result and therefore decided on intense pulsed light therapy.

Hair type: Very dark coarse deep terminal, very curly hair.
Skin type: IV Mediterranean origin.
Treatment method: Intense pulsed light therapy.
Time: 45 minutes.

Treatment plan:	Test patch	Treatment 1	Treatment 2
Fluence	35	39	40
Filter (bikini)	645	645	645
Filter (inner thigh)	695	695	695
Pulses	2	2	2
Duration	5	5	5
Delay	20–30	20–30	20–30

Treatment interval at 8 weeks apart, responding well to treatment.

Client Profile No 11

Age:	43 years.
Sex:	Female.
Nationality:	British.
Medical condition:	Known and noted.
Occupation:	Housewife.
Treatment area:	Chin and top lip.
Probable cause:	Topical stimulation and unknown.

Client had previously plucked hairgrowth.

Hair type:	Dark brown coarse deep terminal hair.
Skin type:	III, sometimes burns but always tans.
Treatment method:	Intense pulsed light therapy.

Time: 30 minutes.

Treatment plan:	Test patch	Treatment 1	Treatment 2
Fluence	45	40	40
Filter	615	615	615
Pulses	3	2	2
Duration	3.2	5	4.5
Delay	25	30	20

Treatment given at interval of 8 weeks.

Client Profile No 12

See Chapter 13 for possible treatment plan for male to female transsexual client.

Model answers

chapter one

Q1 Hereditary.
Topical stimulation, for example waxing.
Medication, for example steroid drugs.
Surgical changes, for example hysterectomy.
Normal systemic changes, for example pregnancy.
Abnormal systemic changes, for example tumours.
Severe emotional trauma, for example divorce.

Q2 85–90% of women remove unwanted hairgrowth.

Q3 Contraceptive pill.
Steroids, Cortisone, Danazol.
Tamoxifen.
Fertility drugs.

Q4 Hirsutism leads to hairgrowth in any of the following male pattern areas.
Toplip, chin and neck areas.
Chest, shoulders and back.

Q5 Androgens increase both the diameter of hairgrowth and its rate of growth.

Q6 Hypertrichosis affects both the male and female sex.

Q7 Genetic.
Racial.
Medication.

Q8 1875

Q9 1980

Q10 Waxing, plucking and shaving.

Q11 Medical support is required in most cases due to unwanted hairgrowth creating low self-esteem leading to psychological problems in may instances.

Q12 Hypertrichosis produces a generalised overgrowth of terminal hairs, which grow longer and faster than normal but are of normal diameter.

chapter **two**

This is a research task hence no answers provided for student task within this chapter.

chapter **three**

Q1 The dermal papilla changes occurring during the hairgrowth cycle are:
Anagen large and active with 2 capillary plexus.
Catagen shrinks and lies isolated below follicle.
Telogen shrinks further and remains isolated below follicle.

Q2 The four main differences between a vellus and terminal hair are:

Vellus	**Terminal**
Fine, soft textured hair.	Dark, thick coarse textured.
Grows from sebaceous gland.	Grows from dermis.
2cm average length.	Can grow several feet in length.
Replacement cycle 8–12 wks.	Replacement cycle 4–6 weeks.
Have a localised blood supply.	Have a deep rich blood supply.
Small root system.	Large root system.

Q3 The dermal cord is formed during the catagen phase of the hairgrowth cycle.

Q4 Krause end bulb sensory corpuscle for cold temperature.
Ruffini corpuscle for heat.

Q5 The layers of the hairshaft are outer cuticle, cortex and medulla.

Q6 Pigmentation of the hair cells occurs during the anagen phase of the hairgrowth cycle only.

Q7 The skin type affects electrolysis treatment in that a sensitive skin will readily accept the current creating an adverse reaction and therefore need careful monitoring.

Q8 Differences between black and white skin include:
Black skin has a thicker epidermis.
Melanin granules secreted by black skin are 4 times larger.
Sebaceous glands more numerous and open directly onto skin surface.
Black skin is able to absorb 70% of ultraviolet radiation.

Q9 The layers of the inner root sheath are:
Cuticle, huxley and henles.

Q10 The two structures which need to remain in contact for regeneration of follicle and hairgrowth are the dermal cord and dermal papilla.

Q11 The 2 layers which comprise the dermis tissue are:
The papillary layer and the reticular layer.

Q12 The dermal protein associated with keloid scarring is collagen.

chapter **four**

This is a research task, hence no answers provided for student task within this chapter.

chapter **five**

Q1 Allows you to probe more accurately.
Prevents eyestrain.
Acts as a breadth shield between you and the client.
Enables you to check condition of needle prior to use.

Q2 To enable you to treat any hair type and length.

Q3 An insulated steel size 3 needle, F31.

Q4 1980 by sterex.

Q5 The hair diameter.
The follicle diameter.
The skin texture.

Q6 Bruising of the tissues as the needle ruptures the blood vessels.

Q7 003 needle.

Q8 Adjustable height.
Vinyl leather for ease of cleaning.
Sturdy construction.

Q9 To enable a high standard of performance.
To prevent injury to the therapist.
For comfort.

Q10 The uni-probe.

Q11 Finger switch.

Foot pedal.

Q12 The services to be offered by therapist.

The cost.

The type of electrode available with unit.

chapter **six**

Q1 Gamma irradiation

Ethylene oxide gas.

Q2 The autoclave.

Q3 Bacteria.

Q4 Hepatitis B, HIV, Influenza and Common cold.

Q5 Staphylococci.

Q6 Warmth, moisture and oxygen to grow.

Q7 To ensure sterilisation is effective.

To remove organic matter.

To remove grease.

Q8 The Local Government (Miscellaneous Provisions) Act.

Q9 Permanent health insurance.

General personal accident insurance.

Critical illness insurance.

Q10 Employers' liability insurance.

Q11 A risk assessment is carried out to assess the risk to others from products hazardous to health.

Q12 Health and Safety At Work Act 1974.

chapter **seven**

Q1 Developing a rapport with the client.

Check client's suitability for treatment.

Able to establish nature of hair problem.

Determine possible cause of hair problem.

Identify previous methods and frequency of hair removal used.

Determine client's expectations of treatment.

Carry out a short test treatment.

Q2 Area treated.

Hair and skin type.

Method used.

Current intensity.

Needle size.

Treatment time.

Skin reaction.

Q3 Good communication skills.

Professional manner and presentation.

Knowledgeable and qualified.

Sympathy and empathy.

Caring and understanding.

Q4 Previous methods of hair removal and frequency of use will impact on the type of hairgrowth present and affect the treatment plan, for example method used, frequency etc.

Q5 Diabetes.

Epilepsy.

Heart conditions.

Hepatitis B.

Unfamiliar medical conditions.

Unfamiliar medications.

Q6 Able to meet and form a rapport with electrologist.

Discuss any fears regarding treatment.

Ask questions about treatment cost and procedures.

Receive a test treatment.

Determine if they are suitable for treatment and if this is the right treatment for them.

Q7 Emotional state.

General health.

Pre-menstrual.

Strength of current.

Area to be treated.

Low blood sugar level.

Q8 Client's body language indicates the clients emotional state, for example fidgeting and lack of eye contact, talking rapidly, or lack of communication indicates nervousness, crossed arms indicates tension, etc.

Q9 Nose and ear areas.

Q10 The client must understand electrolysis is a course of treatment and not a one-off miracle cure, or else they will become despondent quickly and discontinue treatment before treatment has had a chance to work.

Q11 Client's lifestyle.

Time and frequency of treatment.

Probable cause of hairgrowth.

Emotional state.

Physical condition of hair and skin.

Method of electrolysis to be used.

Q12 To track progress of treatment

For legal reasons, for example insurance requirements etc.

chapter eight

Q1 Good stretch.

Probing at the same angle as hairgrowth.

Insert under the hair.

Slide to base of follicle.

Discharge current.

Stretch and epilate.

Q2 Teardrop shape/peardrop shape.

Q3 High percentage of regrowth hairs.

Blanching of the skin tissues.

Q4 Inaccurate probing technique.

Missed hairs.

Accurate probe with insufficient current intensity.

Insufficient length of current application time.

Q5 Tissues fine and thin.

Numerous blood capillaries in brow area.

Hairgrowth usually shallow.

Q6 Opens the follicle mouth to allow smooth insertion on entry.

When removing treated hair, the stretch allows the hair to slide out of the follicle with ease.

Q7 Accurate probing technique.
Accurate current intensity.
Correct current application time.

Q8 Probing too shallow leads to superficial scarring.
Probing too deep leads to pitted scarring.

Q9 Client pain threshold.
Area to be treated.
Hair type and texture.
Skin type and sensitivity.

Q10 By increasing the current application time the heating pattern increases in diameter and length climbing towards skin surface.

Q11 When the moisture gradient of the skin is high, the current will be readily conducted by the skin tissues and care is required with current intensity and application time to prevent the current from reaching the surface tissues and causing blistering.

Q12 The angle of hairgrowth varies between 10 and 90 degrees depending on the area where it arises.

chapter **nine**

Q1 Short wave diathermy would be most suited to fine shallow hair growth on the top lip, rather than the blend due to the probing technique being shallow in depth.

Q2 Sodium hydroxide.
Hydrochloric acid.
Hydrogen gas.
Chlorine gas.

Q3 The high frequency current generates thermal heat which warms the sodium hydroxide and speeds up its chemical action.

Q4 Lye.

Q5 The blend, due to its chemical action.

Q6 A direct current.

Q7 Thermal heat is produced as a result of the high frequency current constantly changing its polarity from negative to positive which causes friction within the tissues creating thermal heat.

Q8 Thermal heats acts on the water molecules of the tissues vaporising them, and the electrical energy produced is absorbed by the proteins in the cells which coagulate the tissues and any blood vessels in the area are cauterised.

Q9 High percentage of regrowth.

Not as effective on curved and distorted hair follicles.

Q10 There is less regrowth than with other forms of electrolysis.

Very effective on distorted curved follicles.

Can be tailored to individual needs of client.

Q11 Fewer hairs treated in one session than short wave diathermy.

Not ideally suited for fine and shallow hairgrowth.

Requires longer treatment session.

Q12 Galvanic/blend.

chapter ten

Q1 Waxing.

Depilatory creams.

Shaving.

Sugaring/threading.

Cutting.

Q2 Laser therapy.

Intense pulsed light therapy.

Q3 Three months or longer.

Q4 Ruby laser.

Alexandrite laser.

Nd Yag laser.

Diode laser.

Q5 Previous exposure to sunlight.

Photo-sensitizing medication.

Some aromatherapy oils, for example citrus based.

Q6 Skin colour and type.

Hair colour and type.

Q7 Hyper-pigmentation of skin tissues.

Blistering of skin tissues.

Q8 Probably due to lack of melanin density in white or blond hair.

Q9 Class I laser.
Q10 Hyper-pigmentation.
    Hypo-pigmentation.
    Mild erythema.
    Localised swelling.
    Blistering.
    Bruising.
Q11 Melanin.
    Blood.
    Water.
Q12 To protect the epidermis.
    Adjust depth of light penetration.

chapter **eleven review tasks**

No answers required for activities.

chapter **twelve**

Q1 This is the treatment of red veins and skin tags by an experienced electrologist.
Q2 Telangiectasia.
Q3 High blood pressure.
    Asthma.
    Diabetes.
    Excess alcohol or spicy foods.
    Sunlight.
    Incorrect skin care products.
    Some types of medication.
    Age, thinning of skin tissues.
    Trauma to skin tissues.
    Hereditary.
    Pregnancy.
    Extremes of temperature.
Q4 Diabetes.
    Aids.

Hepatitis B.

Haemophilia.

Keloid scarring.

Fine fragile thin skin tissues.

Medication, aspirin and anti-coagulants.

Q5 The technique involves tapping into blood capillaries rather than entering the hair follicle, to seal the blood vessel.

Q6 A fibrous growth of epithelial skin tissue which varies in size, shape and colour.

Q7 005, 006, and 010 needles can be used to treat skin tags successfully.

Q8 The facial areas.

The neck region.

The legs.

Q9 The neck region.

The axilla areas.

Q10 Advanced treatments cover, on top of treatment risk insurance.

Q11 Keep the area dry for 24 hours.

Do not touch the skin or pick the scabs.

Apply an antiseptic soothing after care product for 24 hours.

Return in 3 to 4 weeks for check up and/or follow-up treatment.

Q12 To allow the skin time to heal properly.

To work areas requiring treatment in rotation, one area at a time.

chapter thirteen

Q1 Someone born biologically either a man or women, but wishes to change their gender.

Q2 Psychological analysis.

Hormone therapy.

Live and work as chosen gender for two years prior to surgery.

Surgery.

Q3 High dosage oestrogen therapy and possibly an androgen suppressant.

Q4 Breast Augmentation.

Removal of testes.

Formation of pseudo vagina.

Q5 The blend. It is more effective on coarse hairgrowth and ideal for distorted follicles, also there is less regrowth than with short wave diathermy and less chance of hyper-pigmentation occurring.

Q6 A checker board fashion, to prevent overworking of skin tissues.

Q7 Breast development.

Pigmentation of areolar.

Redistribution of body fat, to form female curves.

Improved skin texture due to reduced sebaceous gland activity and the effect of oestrogen levels.

Improved hair texture due to oestrogen also.

Q8 The electrologist is not required for this type of gender reassignment, as hairgrowth is required to make the appearance of the individual more masculine.

Q9 No, not really. Treatment can take anywhere from two to five years as a general guideline.

Q10 The emotional state of the client. They may be prone to mood swings due to the hormone therapy and the stress involved in this type of treatment.

The length of treatment time.

The blend of currents and the role of galvanic treatment.

The needle size.

The skin reaction.

Appointment times.

Q11 The person who referred client to electrologist, for example

The GP

The psychiatrist.

The hospital consultant.

Q12 To ensure that gender reassigment is necessary for individual.

To help transexual adjust to changes occurring as a result of the decision to have gender reassignment, for example hormone therapy and its effects, physiologically, psychologically and physically.

Major upheavals in personal life, for example loss of long-term relationships, career change, new friendships etc.

Glossary

A

Acid Mantle: has a P.H. of 5.4–5.6 and protects the skin against bacterial invasion.

Acne Rosacea: affects nose and cheeks, papules and broken capillaries.

Acne Vulgaris: inflammation of the sebaceous glands.

Adrenal: adrenal gland located capping each kidney.

Adrenaline: a hormone produced in the adrenal medulla.

Albinism: absence of pigment in skin, hair and eyes.

Aldoesterone: an adreno-cortical steroid.

Allergen: any agent capable of producing a state of allergy.

Alpha cell: an islet of langerhan cell responsible for producing the hormone glucagon.

Alopecia: baldness.

Amenorrhoea: lack of periods/menstruation.

Anagen: the stage of hairgrowth.

Androgen: a male hormone.

Angioma: a swelling or tumour caused by blood vessel dilation.

Aorta: the main artery leaving the heart.

Arrector pili muscle: small muscle which contracts the hair.

Asthma: disease which constricts the bronchioles, wheezing results.

Atrophy: thinning or wasting of the tissues.

B

Bacteria: microbes or germs.

Basal cell carcinoma: skin cancer found between eye and nasal line.

Beta cells: an islet of langerhan cell responsible for producing the hormone insulin.

Blend: a method of epilation using a combination of electrical currents to remove unwanted hairgrowth.

Boil: furuncle, an abscess caused by bacteria entering hair follicle.

Bulla: large blister.

C

Capillary: a minute blood vessel.

Carcinoma: a cancerous growth.

Carotenaemia: yellow pigmentatation of the skin tissues.

Carotid artery: the main artery of the neck.

Catagen: the transitory stage of hairgrowth, where the follicle undergoes rapid changes.

Cataracts: an opacity of the crystalline lens or its capsule.

Caustic: an agent that burns or chars the tissues.

Cauterization: the application a high intensity of high frequency current to an area which burns the tissues and vapourises any moisture within area.

Cholasma: irregular brown pigmentation marks.

Cholesterol: a crystalline substance fatty in nature. Found in bile, blood, brain, liver etc when irridated forms vitamin D.

Coagulate: to cause a fluid substance such as blood to become a semi-solid mass.

Collagen: dermal protein forming the connective tissue.

Conductor: a medium which conveys electricity.

Congenital: a condition existing at birth, hereditary.

Consultation: indepth conversation to discuss a proposed treatment.

Contra-indication: a condition which prohibits or restricts treatment.

Cretinism: this is the result of a congenital thyroid deficiency which leads to the underdevelopment of mental and physical growth of an infant.

Cross-infection: the transfer of infection from one person to another or to an object.

Corpus luteum: yellow body formed in the ovary after the rupture of the graafian follicle.

Cortisol: hydrocortisone, an adrenal cortical steriod essential to life.

Cortisone: a powerful steriod hormone found within the adrenal cortex.

Cyst: a sac with a membraneous wall enclosing either fluid or semi-solid matter.

D

Dehydrated: lacking moisture or fat.

Dermal cord: a column of cells which connect the dermal papilla to the hair follicle in the catagen and telogen stages of the hairgrowth cycle.

Dermal papilla: the blood supply to the hair follicle.

Diabetes mellitus: a condition brought about by an imbalance within the sugar metabolism.

Differentiation: the process of change that cells undertake.

Dysmenorrhoea: painful periods.

E

Eczema: an inflammatory condition of the skin tissues.

Epilepsy: results from a disorder of the electrical activity of the brain which brings abouts fits and loss of consciousness.

Electromagnetic spectrum: is composed of a variety of electromagnetic waves and includes visible and invisible light rays of varying lengths.

Ethylene oxide gas: used as a sterilising agent.

Erythema: reddening of the skin tissues.

Enzyme: soluble colloidal protein produced by living cells.

F

Fibro blast cell: responsible for the production of collagen and elastin fibres.

Fissure: a crack in the skin's surface.

Florid: high colouring, redness.

Follicle stimulating hormone: a gonadtotrophic hormone secreted by the anterior lobe of the pituitary gland.

Folliculitus: inflammation of the hair follicles.

G

Gamma irradiation: electromagnetic rays emitted by certain radioactive isotopes used to sterilise.

Glucose: sugar/syrup.

Goitre: a swelling located in the neck associated with thyroid abnormalities.

Graafian follicle: located in the ovary and each contains an ovum/egg.

H

Haemoglobin: the colouring matter of blood.

Haemophilia: an inherited bleeding condition, where there is a defect in the blood clotting mechanism. Affects males only while females are the carriers of this disease.

Hair bulb: lower portion of the hair follicle where mitosis and keratinisation occur.

Hairgrowth cycle: the phases of growth, change and rest that the hair follicle goes through during its life.

Hair matrix: the inner part of the hair.

Hazardous: Dangerous/harmful.

Herpes simplex: a viral infection of the mouth and surrouding area.

Herpes zoster: shingles, a virus related to the chicken pox virus.

Hepatitis B: a viral infection affecting the liver.

Hirsuitism: a male hairgrowth pattern found in women, associated with a hormone imbalance.

Hormone: A chemical messenger.

Hyaline: a membrane.

Hydrochloric acid: a chemical produced during chemical process of electrolysis.

Hyper: excess, above normal.

Hyperkeratosis: excessive thickening of the epidermis.

Hyper-pigmentation: an area of dark pigmentation.

Hypertension: high blood pressure.

Hypertrichosis: affects both sexes, and is the general overgrowth of vellus and terminal hairgrowth.

Hypo: lacking, less than normal.

Hypo-pigmentation: an area lighter than the surrounding skin tissues.

I

Immunization: innoculation against disease, the process of increasing the specific antibody in the tissues.

Impetigo: caused by either a streptoccocal or staphloccocal bacteria which results in a highly contagious skin disease.

Infection: the invassion of the body tissues by disease.

Infrared rays: belong to the electromagnetic spectrum lying outside of the visible spectrum and below the red rays.

Insulator: is something which prevents the passage of electricity passing along it, for example rubber.

Insulin: a hormone produced by the beta cells in the islet of langerhan.

Intense pulsed light therapy: is photothermolysis which uses parallel light waves of varying light to generate heat within the skin tissues and destroy hairgrowth.

Intensity: the amount of energy of heat or light.

Iodine: a powerful antiseptic used as a tincture for skin preparations.

J

Joules: a system for measuring energy, work and quantity of heat.

K

Keloid scar: A fibrous growth of tissue arising from scar tissue.

Keratin Eu: hard keratin found in the nails.

Keratin pseudo: soft keratin found in inner root sheath and hair.

Keratinisation: conversion into horny tissue.

Kertohyaline granules: found immediately below horny layer and a precurser to keratin.

Ketones: are bodies found in the blood and urine. They are structual formulae of organic compounds, for example kerosteroids.

L

Linea nigra: a pigmented line between the umbilicus and pubis which appears during pregnancy.

Lye: another name for sodium hydroxide.

Lymphocytes: a variety of white blood cell.

Lysosomes: found within all cells, produces an enzyme which breaks down cell waste material for reabsorption.

M

Macrophages: a phagocytic cell which plays an important part in organisation and repair of tissue.

Malignant: cancerous growth.

Melanin: the pigment or colour found in hair and skin.

Melanocytes: cells which produce melanin.

Menopause: cessation of menstruation.

Microhaemorrage: a small blood spot.

Micro-organisms: tiny living cells.

Milliamper: one thousandth of an ampere.

Mitosis: cell division.

Mole: a pigmented area on the skin.

N

Neurons: a structual unit of the nervous system comprising of fibres which convey impulses to the nerve cells.

Nucleus: the active centre of cells.

O

Oedema: swelling, fluid retention within the tissues.

Oestrogen: a steroid hormone produced by the ovaries, and a small quantity by the adrenal cortex.

Ostoporosis: loss of bone density.

Oligomenorrhoea: infrequent menstruation, normally 35 days or more per cycle.

Opaque: impervious to light rays, neither transparent nor translucent.

Organism: any living thing either animal or vegetable.

Ossification: the conversion of cartilage etc into bone.

Ovuum: an egg.

Ozone: a form of oxygen that has powerful oxidising properties and is therefore a disinfectant.

P

Paget's disease: a bone disease where the bones are thin due to rapid bone formation.

Papillary layer: the outer layer of the dermis.

Parasite: a living organism which lives on a living host and draws nourishment from that host.

Ph: the scale used to measure acidity and alkaline levels.

Photosensitisation: sensitivity to sunlight, which causes a skin reaction.

Pilosebaceous unit: formed from the hair follicle and sebaceous gland.

Porous: to absorb moisture.

Polycystic ovaries: a disease which causes multiple follicular ovarian cysts, and is associated with infertility.

R

Regrowth hair: hair which has previously been treated and removed, then regrows.

Reticular layer: inner layer of dermis.

Ringworm: a fungal disease.

S

Sclerotherapy: a chemical treatment for varicose veins.

Sebum: an oily substance secreted by the sebaceous glands.

Sensation: a feeling experience as a result of sensory nerve stimulation.

Sensory nerve endings: nerves which carry sensory impulses to the central nervous system.

SPF: sun protection factor, which protects the skin against sunburn.

Sodium hydroxide: also known as lye, a caustic chemical.

Squamous cell carcinoma: a cancerous tumour which arises in the squamous cell tissue.

Stein levanthal syndrome: another name for polycystic ovary syndrome.

Sterilisation: process of achieving total destruction of all living organisms.

Stroma: part of the ovary.

Superfluous: Unwanted/excess.

Synapse: the point of communication between two adjacent neurons.

Systemic: pertaining to a system or to the body as a whole.

T

Thermal: relating to heat.

Thyroxine: a hormone produced by the thyroid gland.

Trachea: windpipe.

Transexual: Someone who wishes to change their gender.

Transient: changing.

Tumour: abnormal growth or swelling.

Tweezers: small forceps.

Tyrosine: an amino acid.

Tyrosinase: an enzyme.

U

Ulcer: an open sore.

Ultra violet: invisible rays of the electro-magnetic spectrum.

Urticaria: hives, rash.

Uterus: womb.

V

Vaporisation: the use of steam vapour to aid the healing of the skin tissues after epilation treatment.

Vasoconstriction: blood vessels constrict.

Vasodilation: blood vessels dilate, rising towards surface.

virgin hair: hair which has not been treated.

Virilisation: manliness.

Virus: a parasitic micro-organism within living cells, leading to infection or disease.

Vitiligo: patches of white skin due to pigment loss.

Varicose veins: swollen or knotted veins.

W

Wet sterilisation: the use of chemical solutions to clean work surfaces etc.

X

Xanthoma: yellow nodules or raised plates on the skin tissue.

Bibiliography

Anatomy and Physiology: by Evelyn Pearce.

Anatomy and Physiology: by Ross and Wilson.

Cosmetic and Medical Electrolysis and Temporary Hair Removal A pratice Manual and Reference Guide: by R.N. Richards M.D. G.E. Merharg R.N.: Medric Ltd.

Complete Guide To Medicine and Clinical Practice, Inside The Human Body.

Electrolysis, Thermolysis And The Blend: by Hinkle and Lind.

Electro-Epilation A Practical Approach For NVQ Level 3 by Elizabeth Cartwright, Gill Morris and Michelle Sullivan.

Epilight Publicity literature.

Essentials Of Dermatology third edition: by J.L. Burton.

The Gender Trust Information Sheet Series.

Hormone treatment for male to female transsexual people.

An introduction to Gender Dysphoria for female to male transsexual people.

Human Physiology and Health: by Morton.

International hair route issue number 85.

Internet sites: Laser technology.

Magazine article: from the health and beauty salon, magazine April 1996 and June 1999.

Magazine article: Guild news April 2001.

The Hirsute Female: by R.B. Greenblatt.

The Institute of Electrolysis Hosting Advanced Initiatives In Hair Removal Lecture.

Principles and techniques for the Electrologist: by Ann Gallant.

The Principles And Practice Of Electrical Epilation: by Shelila Godfrey.

The Science of Beauty Therapy: by Ruth Bennette.

The Standard textbook for Professional Estheticians: by Joel Gerson.

Sterilisation and Hygiene: by W.G. Peberdy.

Telangiectasia Procedures To Remove Dilated Blood Vessels Using The Blend Method: by Michael Bono: Tortoise Press.

The Structure and function of the skin third edition: by Montagna Parakkal.

Therapeutic lasers, Theory and Practice: by G. David Baxter.

Thermolase UK Ltd (softlight) Publicity literature.

Understanding HRT and Menopause: by Dr Robert Wilson.

Useful Addresses

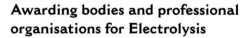

Awarding bodies and professional organisations for Electrolysis

The Institute of Electrolysis
138 Downs Barn Boulevard,
Downs Barn,
Milton Keynes,
MK14 7RP

Telephone: 01908 695297

The British Association of Electrolysists
(BAE)
2A Tudor Way,
Hillingdon,
Uxbridge,
UX10 9AB

Telephone: 01895 239966

Sterex Academy
Exhall,
Coventry,
Warwickshire,
CV7 9QW

Awarding bodies and professional organisations for beauty therapy

City and Guilds of London Institute
1 Giltspur Street
London

Telephone: 0207 294 2468

Confederation of Beauty Therapy and
    Cosmetology (CIBTAC)
Parabola House,
Parabola Road,
Gloucester,
GL50 3AH

International Therapy Examination
    Council (ITEC)
10–11 Heathfield Terrace
Chiswick
London
W4 4JE

Telephone: 0208 994 4141.

Business and Technical Education Council
    (B. TEC)
Tavistock House South
Entrance D
London
WC1H 9LG

Vocational Training Charitable Trust and
    Vocational
Awards International LTD (VAI)
46 Aldwick Road,
Bognor Regis
West Sussex
PO21 2PN and also

Unit 11
Brickfield Trading Estate,
Brickfield Lane
Chandlers Ford
Hampshire
SO53 4DR

Edexcel
Stewart House,
32 Russel Square,
London,
WC1B 5DN.

National Council for Vocational
    Qualification
222 Euston Road
London
NW1 2BZ

Other Professional Associations

British Association of Beauty Therapy and
    Cosmetology (BABTEC)
Babtec House
70 Eastgate Street,
Gloucester.
GL1 1QN

International Federation of Health and
    Beauty Therapists (IFHB)
3rd Floor,
Eastleigh House,
Upper Market Street,
Eastleigh
Hampshire,
SO50 9FD

Guild of Professional Beauty Therapists
PO Box 310
Derby
DE23 6ZT

Suppliers of Electrolysis Equipment

Sterex Electrolysis International Limited
174 Kings Road,
Tyseley,
Birmingham,
B11 2AP
Telephone: 01203 362930

Ellisons
43 Bayton Road,
Exhall,
Coventry,
CV7 9EF
Telephone: 024 7636 1619

The Hairdressing and Beauty Equipment
    Centre
262 Holloway Road,
London
N7 6NE
Telephone: 020 607 7475

Taylor Reeson Laboratories LTD
Carlton House,
Commerce Way
Lancing,
West Sussex
Telephone: 01903 761100

DU-LAC
1 Albion Villas,
The Leas,
Folkestone,
Kent.
Telephone: 01303 254431

Bretherton
29 Orchard Road
Beeston
Sandy,
Bedfordshire,
SG19 1PJ
Telephone: 01767 680041

Sorisa
Bellissima Inc Limited,
Bellissima House,
212 Northenden Road,
Sale,
Cheshire
M33 2PA
Telephone: 0161 976 4614

Laser Suppliers

Epilight
Arden Medical
12 Upper Parliament Street,
Nottingham,
NG1 2AD
Telephone: 0115 950 5084

Visulase
CACI International
11 Heath Street,
Hampstead,
London,
NW3 6TP
Telephone: 020 7431 1033

Aculight UK Ltd,
Merit House,
Edgeware Road,
Colindale,
London,
NW9 5AF
Telephone: 0800 0920876

Depilase UK Ltd
1 Canada Square,
Canary Wharf,
London
E14 5DY
Telephone: 020 7712 1675

Red Beam Laser
Scanda Sol Professional
12–14 Legge Lane,
Birmingham,
B1 3LD
Telephone: 0121 685 1551

Smartepil
Biofarm UK
54 Lambs Conduit Street,
London,
WC1N 3LL
Telephone: 020 74058668

Softlight by
Thermolase UK Ltd,
45–47 Cheval Place,
Knightsbridge,
London
SW7 1EW
Telephone: 0207581 4499

Plasmalite
Focuslaser
8 Buckland Cresent
London
NW3 5DW

Telephone: 0207 722 1758

Epil Pro
Depache Mode
Laborratories Ltd,
8 Chestnut Close
Maidenhead,
Berks
SL6 8SY

Telephone: 01628 674 644

Depilite
Cosmeceuticals
3 Swinborne Court,
Swinborne Road,
Basildon,
Essex,
SS13 1QA

Telephone: 01268 7244

Index